ENGLISH HERITAGE

PESTS
IN HOUSES GREAT & SMALL

IDENTIFICATION, PREVENTION, ERADICATION

DAVID PINNIGER AND DEE LAUDER

Commissioned by the Curatorial Department
© English Heritage 2018
First published by
English Heritage 2018
100 Wood Street
London EC2V 7AN

Editor: Jennifer Cryer
Designer: Martin Brown
Cover Design: Two Associates
Printed in England by Page Bros, Norwich
C10 05/21 502927
ISBN 978 1 910907 24 5

About the Authors

David Pinniger's passion for insects started as a boy when he helped his amateur entomologist father catch, identify and release dragonflies. He started work as a food inspector with the Ministry of Agriculture Fisheries and Food (MAFF) and then as a research scientist for the MAFF Central Science Laboratory in Slough. In 1996 he became an independent consultant providing specialist advice and training on pests in museums, galleries, archives and historic houses. He is the pest management strategy adviser for English Heritage and advises many national museums, galleries and historic houses in the UK.  David has worked with overseas museums and presented at conferences and training workshops in many countries. He is the author of over 60 papers and publications.

David is a Fellow of the Royal Entomological Society. He was awarded the 2008 Plowden Medal for his contribution to preventive conservation and received an MBE in the Queen's 2008 Birthday Honours list.

David's hobbies include a love of narrow-gauge steam trains, in full size and on his garden railway, and photography of trains and wildlife.

Dee Lauder has worked for English Heritage since March 1989. She joined the Collections Conservation Team in 2001 and in 2003 was appointed to lead the delivery of English Heritage's Integrated Pest Management (IPM) Programme and IPM standards. Dee's role involves implementing control methods for sites with collections, as well as giving advice on insect pest identification, monitoring and treatment methods appropriate for significant and historic collections. She also undertakes training in these areas for English Heritage staff. In addition, she provides IPM advice to  organisations and individuals outside English Heritage and is a member of the Pest Odyssey UK Steering Committee, a non-profit organisation advocating IPM in cultural heritage institutions.

Her hobbies include longstanding passions for medieval and Tudor history, notably for Richard III and the six wives of Henry VIII, and for punk, indie and rock music, particularly from the 1970s and 1980s. She is a lifelong supporter of Leeds United Football Club and avidly follows European football and the World Cup.

FOREWORD

This book embodies the wealth of experience gained over many years at English Heritage in preventing pests from causing damage to historic house collections. It gives me great pleasure to be able to share with you the intriguing world of insect and other pests, which are perfectly adapted to feast on and damage the objects most precious to us.

I was inducted to this world in 1995 when I was fortunate to attend a five-day residential course about Integrated Pest Management (IPM), which was a newly

(Below) **A felt cockerel tea cosy damaged by insect pests**

emerging field within preventive conservation. The loss of a range of toxic insecticides and fumigants provoked the need for a new approach to controlling insect pests, based on monitoring, targeted cleaning and treatments non-toxic to humans. It was where I first met David Pinniger, one of the authors of this book, who inspired and coached me to deploy IPM at English Heritage properties. Placing sticky insect blunder traps throughout the enormous Audley End House near Cambridge started me on a journey that transformed both the care of collections at English Heritage, and my own career. I still remember the mixture of excitement and dread on catching 'woolly bears' – the larvae of the carpet beetle *Anthrenus verbasci* – and then the satisfaction of preventing damage to historic carpets and curtains through finding and removing their food source, which turned out to be masses of dead flies trapped in window box seats.

Over the past 20 years there have been many more examples of IPM preventing damage to collections and buildings in the care of English Heritage, some of which are described in this book. In 2003 Dee Lauder, the co-author of this book, took over the management of English Heritage's IPM programme, expanding the number of properties monitored from six to seventy and developing her practical experience and knowledge along the way.

At the heart of the IPM process are the pests themselves, and understanding their needs and being able to identify them is key to control. So you will need to tap into your inner entomologist using the wonderful images in this book as a guide. The wealth of information and practical tips shared so expertly by David and Dee will help you to prevent damage either to your own homes and belongings or in a grand country house open to the public.

Amber Xavier-Rowe
Head of Collections Conservation, English Heritage

INTRODUCTION

Humans versus pests: an age-old conflict

Humans have been fighting a battle against pests ever since we started to wear clothes, live in dwellings and store food. A pest can be defined simply as an animal living in the wrong place at the wrong time and many of our most troublesome pest species cause no problems to humans when they are living in their natural outdoor habitats, such as a bird's nest or a fallen log. Our houses, however, provide a warm, sheltered environment with abundant food and few predators – a far more attractive habitat for many species in which to thrive and multiply than the great outdoors.

The first historical records of pests infesting homes are from Greek and Roman times. Roman writers, such as Cato the Elder (writing in the second century BC), Pliny and Columella (writing in the first century AD) recommended many different methods for killing pests. These ranged from religious rituals carried out under a full moon, to the use of fly swatters and chemicals, such as burning sulphur, and the application of amurca (the sediment, or lees, that settles from unfiltered olive oil). Some of these suggestions were more effective than others: sulphur is toxic to most animals and olive oil lees has an insecticidal effect. Natural insect repellents used in Roman times included rosemary and juniper.

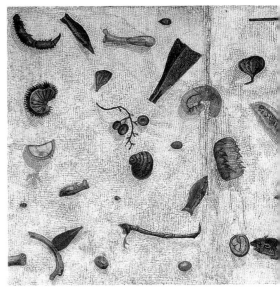

(Above) This second-century mosaic, from the dining room of a Roman villa, depicts the remains of a feast, with a house mouse nibbling a discarded walnut – presumably a common sight

> 'To protect clothing from moths: boil amurca down to one-half its volume and rub it over the bottom, the outside, the feet, and the corners of the chest. After it is dry, store the clothing and the moths will not attack it.'
>
> **Cato the Elder, *de Agri Cultura*, c.160 BC.**

'The moth breeds among clothes till
that they have bitten it asunder and
it is a maniable [flexible] *worm,*
and yet it hides him in the cloth that
it can scantly be seen and it breeds
gladly in clothes that have been in an
evil air, or in a rain or mist, and so laid
up without hanging in the sun or
other sweet air after.

The herbs that be bitter and
well smelling is good to be laid
among such clothes as the bay leaves,
cypress wood.'

**Quotation written in modern
English from Laurence Andrew,
*The Noble Lyfe and Natures of Man,
of Bestes, Serpentys, Fowles and
Fisshes yt be Moste Knowen,* 1521;
an English translation of a text
from 1491.**

**(Above) Woodcut showing clothes damaged
by moths, in the late-15th-century book
from which Laurence Andrew's text was
translated**

These Classical texts were preserved in compilations
of agricultural lore throughout the early Middle Ages and
in medieval times there were many books and manuals
offering advice on the best methods for preserving
possessions and buildings against attacks by pests. Many
advocated physical methods, such as beating carpets to
kill clothes moths and carbonising the outside of wooden
beams to prevent wood-boring beetles and mould, as
well as the application of herbs and other botanicals, such
as lavender and tobacco. Although such methods would
have had some effect on reducing damage, it was not until
an understanding of chemistry was established in the
19th century that really effective insecticide treatments
were discovered.

From the 16th century onwards, the mania for
collecting specimens of animals, plants and ethnographic
objects from faraway places had the most dramatic

effect on the development of preservatives. Collectors such as John Tradescant, whose collection formed the basis of the first museum in England, the *Musaeum Tradescantianum*, first catalogued in about 1656, assembled 'cabinets of curiosities' filled with exotic specimens. It would have been pointless to collect such objects, however, if they were reduced to debris and dust by the end of a long sea voyage. Mercury, arsenic and sulphur compounds were all in the travelling collector's armoury and specimens from the 18th century, such as a Maori cloak given to Captain Cook, made from extinct moa bird feathers, still survive because the toxic chemicals applied to them protected them from damage by insect pests. The first published manual for collectors was *The Naturalist's and Traveller's Companion, Containing Instructions for Discovering*

(Top) **A 'cabinet of curiosities' of natural and ethnographic objects collected by Danish antiquary Ole Worm, illustrated in his book *Museum Wormianum*, 1655** *(Above)* **Carabid beetle collected in Chile by Charles Darwin during his voyage on HMS *Beagle***

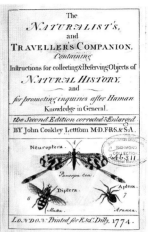

'After our insects are properly dried, they may be placed in the cabinet or boxes where they are to remain – these boxes should be kept dry, and also made to shut very close to prevent small insects from destroying them, the bottoms of the boxes should be … lined with cork, well impregnated with a solution of a quarter of an ounce of corrosive sublimate mercury [mercury (II) chloride], in half that quantity of aetherial oil of turpentine, and a pint of the camphorated spirit of wine.'

The Naturalist's and Traveller's Companion …
John Coakley Lettsom, London, 1772.

(Above) The title page of the 1774 edition of John Coakley Lettsom's book, *The Naturalist's and Traveller's Companion*

and Preserving Objects of Natural History by John Coakley Lettsom, published in 1772.

In the 18th century, some of these chemicals were also being used to treat fine textiles and taxidermy in grand houses, but it was not until the rise of the chemical industry in the 19th century that insecticides and rodenticides became more widely available and affordable. Some of these chemicals, such as nicotine, rotenone (derived from derris) and pyrethrum, were obtained from plants. Although large quantities of chemicals were sold for moth proofing, killing flies and eradicating rodents, physical methods were also employed, including fly screens, cockroach traps and the use of cold stores to store furs in the hot summer months. Some of these techniques are still used today, although the use of many highly toxic chemicals, such as arsenic and strychnine, has long since been banned.

The Second World War was a significant stimulus to the chemical industry and led to the development of the first generation of synthetic pesticides, DDT (dichlorodiphenyltrichloroethane) being the best known and perhaps the most notorious. This chemical and its derivative lindane, or gamma HCH, were responsible for saving millions of lives by eradicating insect-borne diseases including malaria and sleeping sickness from large areas of the world. Lindane was also used in very large quantities in houses to treat timber infested with furniture beetles and deathwatch beetles. Pesticides were thought to be the answer to all pest problems and were incorporated into everyday household products, such as a liquid window cleaner that killed flies when they landed on windows.

American biologist Rachel Carson's seminal book *Silent Spring*, published in 1962, was a wake-up call

(Above) A 1950s bottle of a DDT-based insecticide
(Below) Advert of 1945

Harold Maxwell-Lefroy

Harold Maxwell-Lefroy (1877– 1925) was appointed Imperial College London's first Professor of Entomology in 1912.

In 1914 he investigated an outbreak of deathwatch beetle in Westminster Hall and devised a chemical remedy against woodworm which he called Ento-kill Fluid. He trademarked the product as 'Rentokil', which became the name of his business, now an internationally known pest control company. Maxwell-Lefroy became a victim of his own inventiveness when he was killed by toxic fumes in his own laboratory in 1925.

20 YEARS *study of* **INSECT PESTS** *at your service*

Exhaustive study of insects in our laboratories and control rooms enables you to protect your stocks and to give your customers death-dealing remedies. Disease carrying and destructive insects can be eradicated by one or other of the authorised

RENTOKIL *Insecticides*

(Reg. Trade Mark)
" **MOTHPROOFER** " for clearing out moth eggs, grubs and flies.
" **R.I.P.** " Insect Powder for flies, lice, ticks, fleas, ants, etc.
" **R.I.P.** " Pets Insect Powder for domestic animals.
" **KILIT** " for tough vermin like bugs, beetles, cockroaches, etc.
" **TIMBERFLUID** " to save furniture from the destructive wood borers.
Enquire for Free advice, prices and terms.
RENTOKIL LTD., 168/170 Stockwell Rd., S.W.9
Manufacturers of Insecticides for over 20 years.

which alerted people to the dangers of DDT and other pesticides persisting in the environment and causing long-term problems. Far more effective and less persistent insecticides were developed in the 1970s and 1980s leading to much safer products. Synthetic pyrethroids were developed as substitutes for natural pyrethrins as natural pyrethrum, one of the few very low-hazard insecticides, was in short supply. The move away from persistent toxicants since the 1970s has also led to a resurgence of interest in desiccant dusts which kill insects by drying them out.

Some people have always preferred to use 'natural' products, but it has to be recognised that some of these can be as toxic as their synthetic counterparts. The use of natural repellents has been revived in recent years, however, with many products now on sale to repel flies, moths and carpet beetles.

(Left) **Rachel Carson photographed in 1963 with her seminal book** *Silent Spring*

Pyrethrum, the oldest insecticide?

One group of chrysanthemums, the pyrethrums, has been exploited for millennia for its amazing insecticidal properties.

The ancient Chinese probably used crushed pyrethrum *Chrysanthemum cinerariifolium* flowers as an insecticide from about 1000 BC. The Persians were using extracts of pyrethrum in 400 BC to control insect pests and in the 19th century the insecticide was known as 'Persian powder'. During the Napoleonic Wars French soldiers used the flowers to deter fleas and body lice.

A group of chemicals called pyrethrins were identified as the key insecticidal components of pyrethrum extract and commercial production of the flowers began in the 1920s. Pyrethrum grows best in mountainous equatorial zones and much of the world's supply of natural pyrethrins comes from Kenya.

Pyrethrin is a potent insect nerve poison causing paralysis and rapid death and at low doses can also have a repellent effect. At the normal doses used to kill insects it has very low toxicity to humans and other mammals, making it one of the safest insecticides known. It also breaks down rapidly in sunlight, leaving no persistent harmful chemicals in the environment.

A drop in production of natural pyrethrins in the 1960s led to a search for synthetic alternatives and a wide range of synthetic pyrethroids, including bioresmethrin, tetramethrin and allethrin is now available. These are often formulated as aerosols or sprays to rapidly knock down and kill flying insects. Other synthetic pyrethroids that persist for much longer, including permethrin, cypermethrin and deltamethrin, can be used as residual sprays or dusts to control crawling insects. Some of these are more toxic to humans, but because they are so potent against insects, they are used at very low doses.

Despite these synthetic alternatives, natural pyrethrins are still produced in large quantities and remain important as they are accepted as organic insecticides and are often the only pesticides allowed in food production and preparation areas.

(Right) **Harvesting pyrethrum flowers, northern Rwanda**

What sort of problems do pests cause?

Pests can be damaging, annoying or even dangerous. It is always advisable to seek professional help to eradicate cockroaches, which are a serious pest worldwide (see page 120). Other pests that attack humans and spread disease, such as fleas, bedbugs and mosquitos, should also be tackled by experts, and are not discussed in this book. The main focus of this guide is to help you to identify and eradicate pests which cause damage to possessions or buildings, and those that can invade our homes, causing annoyance and distress when they are present in large numbers.

Materials that are vulnerable to attack by these types of pests include:

- **Wool** Clothes, carpets and upholstery
- **Fur** Clothes and taxidermy
- **Feathers** Clothes and taxidermy
- **Silk** Clothes and wall coverings
- **Dried plant material** Baskets, dried plants and food
- **Paper** Books, photographs, wallpaper and archives
- **Wood** Furniture, flooring, picture frames and structural timber
- **Electrical wiring and cables**

(Below) **Victorian display of bird taxidermy devastated by clothes moths**

Different insects attack these different materials and damage can range from a few holes eaten in a felt hat or a favourite jumper by carpet beetle larvae, to the wholesale destruction of valuable rugs or carpets by clothes moth larvae, or a floorboard by furniture beetles. Mice and other rodents can also damage our possessions by gnawing and cause great nuisance and distress by contaminating food and creating a health hazard.

Some pests also act as useful warning signs that there are problems with the structure or maintenance of a house. Large numbers of silverfish and mould feeders, such as fungus beetles, will only be present when there are high levels of moisture. This may be from leaks or damp ingress through walls or from condensation. When these structural problems are rectified, pest numbers will drop and eventually die away as their favoured living conditions disappear. Furniture beetle damage is evident in many old houses, but the beetles will not survive in dry wood and only thrive when conditions are right. Deathwatch beetles require oak which has been really damp and has been attacked by fungus. Increase in activity of either of these

(Below) **A wool and silk carpet being eaten by clothes moth larvae**

pests is a sign that there is a structural or maintenance problem that needs sorting out.

Most pest species require specific habitats and conditions to survive, and if our homes provide these conditions, infestations can occur.

How will this book help?

This guide will help you to prevent pest infestation and avoid problems developing, identify which pests might be present in your house, and suggest methods to combat them. The three key stages for successful pest management are:

1. Know your enemy:
- Look out for signs of pests: what damage are they causing?
- Identify the pest species.
- Find out where and why they are living in your house.

2. Solve the problem: what can we do to stop pests causing damage?
- Understand which pests you are targeting and control the population.
- Make your home an inhospitable habitat for pests by removing sources of food, shelter or moisture.
- Kill pests by carrying out appropriate treatments on affected objects or the building itself.

3. Stop pests returning:
- Proof your house to stop the pests getting in.
- Carry out regular housekeeping and maintenance.
- Use appropriate deterrents to discourage pests.

(Below) **Severe damage to a wooden floorboard caused by furniture beetles**

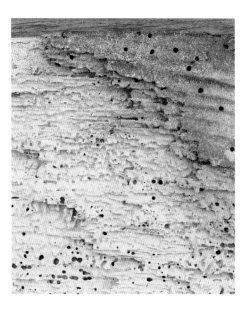

PEST IDENTIFICATION GUIDE

The first step towards successful pest management is to identify exactly which species is causing damage to your possessions and property, and to look out for new species invading your home. Correct identification is essential for successful treatment. Rodents and birds are usually easy to identify, but insects can be more difficult and careful observation and understanding of their life cycles is required to prevent and control infestations.

This pest identification guide will help you to identify the key pest species at all stages of their life cycles.

Insects: an ancient group of organisms

Insects in houses can be annoying and damaging, but most insects in the world are not pests and many are essential to the balanced ecology of our planet. Of the hundreds of thousands of different species, only a very small number come into direct conflict with man. To understand the pests that we encounter in our houses we need to look at the bigger picture of the amazing variety of insects, what they need to survive, and how their life cycles work.

Insects are an ancient group dating back 300 million years to the Carboniferous period. Fossilised species of cockroaches and silverfish that lived millions of years ago are very similar to present-day species. They thrived on eating decaying organic matter, a niche they still exploit today. Beetles and moths arrived later on the geological scene, probably closely connected to the evolution of flowering plants over 30 million years ago. Some species of wood-boring beetles, found fossilised in amber, lived happily in dead trees and fallen logs well before human beings even existed.

(Below) **A fossil silverfish preserved for millions of years in a piece of Baltic amber**

The rise of insect pests

Most of our beetle and moth pests became more closely associated with man as we abandoned our hunter-gatherer nomadic lifestyles for a more settled agriculture-based existence about 11,000 years ago. Houses, clothes, domestic animals and stored produce all provided a ready source of food for many species which we now call pests. The first physical evidence of modern-day household pests, such as biscuit beetles and hide beetles, are from Egyptian tomb burials from at least 1000 BC, and archaeological evidence suggests that the Romans spread clothes moths and other pests around Europe as they expanded their empire from the first century BC to the second century AD.

Many of the commonest pest species were well established in homes of all types from the Middle Ages onwards. The huge increase in trade in the 19th century with the Industrial Revolution providing larger and faster ships to carry tea, grain and wool gave insect pests an opportunity to travel with the goods they were infesting and spread to countries where they had not previously

(Above) **A biscuit beetle preserved in a loaf of funerary bread, from an Egyptian tomb of about 1500 to 1000 BC**

been found. The Australian spider beetle *Ptinus tectus*, for example, was so-named because it was found on grain ships coming from Australia. Like many common insect names, however, this one is inappropriate, as the species originated in Northern Europe. It probably hitched a ride on ships going to Australia, became established in grain residues left in ships' holds and then infested the Australian grain on its way back to Britain.

One of our most important household pests, the webbing clothes moth, was not known in Britain in the 18th century and was probably introduced in the 19th century on imported skins and feathers from South Africa. It then became established across Europe, but has only recently become the most serious textile pest in Britain.

Urbanisation in the 19th century was also a big influence on the success and proliferation of many species of insect pests such as cockroaches, fleas and bedbugs. The rapid growth of towns and cities, mass production of wool carpets and accumulation of possessions kept in warm houses provided pests such as carpet beetles and clothes moths with an almost inexhaustible food supply.

Although many pest species are ubiquitous, there are still some distinct differences between pests found in different climatic areas. Termites, for example, cause significant damage to buildings, but are generally found only in tropical and sub-tropical countries. There have been many changes in the distribution of pests in recent years, however, with new pest species being seen in Britain for the first time, and already-established species expanding their ranges to more northerly areas.

(Above) **Animal skins imported from Africa were probably responsible for the introduction of webbing clothes moths into Britain in the 19th century**

Which types of insects are pests?

Insects are the largest section in the group of animals called arthropods, meaning 'jointed limbs', and they are also sometimes called 'hexapoda' because they have six legs. Although the term 'bug' is frequently used to describe any insect, it should only really be applied to one group of insects called Hemiptera, which have sucking mouth parts. This group includes pest species such as bedbugs, and plant bugs such as aphids. The majority of insect pest species in our homes are not, therefore, 'bugs', but are from other insect groups, classified according to their life cycles and body forms. The major groups of insects that cause problems in houses are beetles (Coleoptera), moths (Lepidoptera), silverfish (Zygentoma or Thysanura) and booklice (Psocoptera). Other types of insects which normally live outdoors, but which will invade houses and cause problems include ants (Hymenoptera) and flies (Diptera). All these types are discussed in the following Pest Identification Guide.

Adult insects have three pairs of jointed legs and have their skeleton on the outside (an exoskeleton), which is a jointed box made of a hard substance called chitin. Many familiar insect species have one or two pairs of membranous wings. In adult beetles, the first pair of wings are hardened into wing cases called elytra, which have a clear dividing line down the back.

Insects have specialised sense organs which are very different from ours. Many species, such as flies, have multi-faceted 'compound' eyes which may not give clear images, but can give near all-round vision and are extremely sensitive to light and movement. The most important sense organs for the majority of insects are the antennae – long, segmented filaments on the head with sensory cells tuned to smell, taste, touch, humidity or heat.

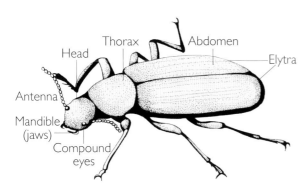

Head
Thorax
Abdomen
Elytra
Antenna
Mandible (jaws)
Compound eyes

(Left) **The anatomy of a beetle**

Reproduction, growth and environment

After mating, female insects lay eggs, sometimes in very large numbers. These hatch into juvenile stages which do not have sex organs or other adult features, such as wings. The juvenile stages may be nymphs, which resemble small adults, or larvae, which look completely different. Because insects have a rigid exoskeleton, they cannot grow gradually to reach the adult stage in the way we do. Instead, they moult, with the juvenile stage shedding outgrown skins many times until the adult stage is reached and the insect does not grow any more. These juvenile stages can often last many weeks, months or even years, hidden away inside the material they are infesting. It is often only when the adults emerge that people realise they have an insect pest problem.

Adults often eat very little in comparison with the growing, immature stages. Cockroaches, silverfish and booklice all develop as nymphs which usually eat similar food to adults. Beetles, moths, ants and flies all develop from larvae which have completely different habits from the adults and usually eat very different food. A carpet beetle larva, for example, requires food of animal origin for growth and development and will eat wool, skin, dead insects and feathers. The adult beetle, on the other hand, eats very

(Below) **Adults and nymphs of the common book louse *Liposcelis* sp. (see page 55)**
(Bottom) **Pupae of vodka beetle, *Attagenus smirnovi* (see page 36)**

little, but has a preference for pollen and nectar from certain wild flowers.

The larvae transform through a series of moults to a sexually mature adult through an intermediate stage called the pupa. This transformation from a worm-like caterpillar to an adult moth or beetle has fascinated people for centuries. Visibility of pests will depend on which stage they have reached in their life cycles. Correct pest identification requires understanding of these different phases, where they might be found and what they look like.

Insects are unable to regulate their own temperature and this can be used to prevent an infestation developing. Growth, feeding and reproduction are more rapid at temperatures above 20°C, but slow down as temperatures are reduced and eventually stop at temperatures below 10°C, although much lower temperatures are required to actually kill pest insects.

Correct identification of pests will improve your chances of successfully controlling or preventing infestation.

(Below) **An adult varied carpet beetle *Anthrenus verbasci* (see page 33) on a flower, feeding on nectar**

Clothes Moths and House Moths

A number of moth species that infest and damage textiles and animal- and plant-based material live in houses in Britain. They are all small and relatively inconspicuous compared with the larger moths we may see attracted to lights in the evening. It is important to be able to identify which species has invaded your home, as they have different habits and food preferences.

Adult moths fly into buildings through windows or open doors and birds' nests are a favourite natural habitat. Dead animals, such as birds and mice, may also provide a source of food and support a moth infestation. The adult moths do not feed and therefore cause no damage; it is the grub-like larvae that feed and damage our clothes and other items. One generation normally takes a year to complete the life cycle, but webbing clothes moths can

(Below) **An upholstered chair attacked by webbing clothes moth larvae, leaving a mess of damaged fabric, webbing, frass and cast pupal cases**

develop more rapidly if they are warm and undisturbed. The pelleted excreta, or frass, produced by the larvae of moths is frequently mistaken for moth eggs. Frass pellets are hard and opaque, however, whereas moth eggs are very small and translucent, and vulnerable to physical damage. Contrary to popular opinion, clothes moth eggs will hatch within a few days and will not remain dormant in textiles and then hatch many months later.

Textiles soiled with food, sweat or urine are preferentially attacked and a stained area may be far more damaged than an adjacent clean one, because the added nutrients have attracted pests. Pure silk is rarely attacked, but damage to silk clothing is sometimes seen under the arms, round the neck and in the groin. Damage is also more concentrated in dark, undisturbed areas, for example where a wool carpet lies under heavy furniture, in crevices and inaccessible places, behind lapels and in pockets of garments, or where carpets or textiles are rolled or folded. Wool insulation in attics and cavity walls can provide a perfect home. Clean cotton materials are not normally attacked.

(Below) **A tiny clothes moth egg hidden in the fibres of a woollen garment**
(Bottom) **The life cycle of a moth: it is the larvae of clothes moths and house moths that cause damage, not the adult moths themselves**

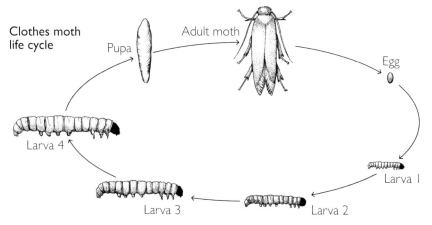

Clothes moth life cycle

Pupa · Adult moth · Egg · Larva 1 · Larva 2 · Larva 3 · Larva 4

Common or webbing clothes moth
Tineola bissefliella

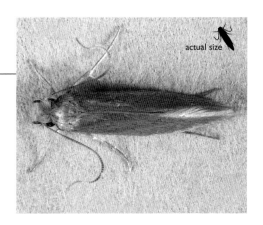

actual size

The common or webbing clothes moth is the most important and damaging of the pest moth species. It was probably introduced into Britain in the 19th century on skins and feathers from South Africa, where it can naturally be found living in animal and bird nests and on bodies of dead animals.

Although it has been a pest for many years, numbers have increased dramatically in the last ten years and it is now a scourge in many houses and museum collections across the whole of the British Isles. The moths are small, shiny and silvery-gold, without markings, and have a brush of gingery-brown hairs on the head. They are about 5–8mm long and seem to scuttle around when disturbed and only fly when it is warm. They shun the light and hide in dark areas.

Each female moth lays batches of up to 100 eggs on fur, feathers, skins, wool or soiled silk. The white grub-like larvae which hatch from the eggs, cause all the damage. The larva produces strands or tunnels of silk webbing which it lays across the attacked material, feeding underneath. Damage by these larvae is either in the form of grazed fabric or irregular, chewed holes. Damage is accompanied by copious webbing tubes or sheets, which usually include a large number of gritty frass pellets. Infestations appear far more 'messy' than the damage caused by other types of moths.

Recorded distribution of webbing clothes moth

actual size

Case study: Webbing clothes moths at Ranger's House

A high count of webbing clothes moths were found on a pheromone lure in the Pink Silk Room at Ranger's House, London, in the winter of 2012.

A thorough check of all the upholstered furniture and a large rug within the room was undertaken, but no further traces of moths, larvae or webbing could be found. All the sticky insect pest traps in this room and the adjacent rooms were checked, but, again, no moths were found and none were seen flying about. Staff also checked and cleaned the curtains and pelmets and reported finding no evidence of moths. We therefore put out three webbing clothes moth pheromone traps in the adjacent rooms and an additional one in the Pink Silk Room, but only a few moths were caught on these.

As a thorough inspection of the rooms and collections had failed to find a source for the moths, we suspected that the moth larvae must be living in the floor voids and structural dead spaces. A few months later a hatch was discovered in the floor of an adjacent room. When this was opened, the carcase of a mouse was found directly underneath, and adult webbing clothes moths were seen flying around in the void. The dead mouse was removed and the area was thoroughly cleaned. Since then, the high numbers of webbing clothes moths have reduced, but we continue to remain vigilant, using pheromone lures to check for new infestations, as well as maintaining a good housekeeping schedule.

Key lessons:

✓ *Using a sticky webbing clothes moth pheromone trap allowed a potential infestation to be identified and prevented before moths were able to cause damage to precious textiles.*

✗ *Using poisoned bait is not always a good way of controlling a mouse or rat infestation: when mice die in floor voids and other inaccessible places, they can provide a food source for other pests.*

✓ *Moths aren't always living in the most obvious places. Thorough checking may be required to find the source of an infestation.*

Case-bearing clothes moth
Tinea pellionella

actual size

Adult case-bearing clothes moths have been in Britain for several thousand years and were possibly introduced with the Romans. Their natural home is birds' nests and animal carcases, but they have readily adapted to living inside our houses.

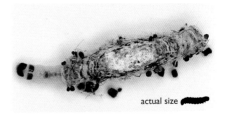

actual size

The adults are silvery-grey with two indistinct dark patches on each wing and a brush of gingery-brown hairs on the head. The case-bearing clothes moth larva spins a cocoon-like casing around itself leaving the ends open so that it can use its jaws and legs. It then eats as it crosses the material, carrying its silk case and leaving a trail of grazed textile or fur with gritty frass pellets. The larva moults within the case and frequently incorporates textile fibres into the case, which may then be a similar colour to the material being damaged. When the larva is fully grown, it pupates within the case and, eventually, the adult moth emerges to mate and lay eggs.

They are similar in size to webbing clothes moths (about 5–8mm long) and also seem to scuttle around when disturbed and only fly when it is warm. Characteristic signs of case-bearing clothes moth are irregular holes in fabric, empty larval cases and gritty frass.

(Right) Woollen mat eaten by case-bearing clothes moth larvae. The empty larval cases are attached to the fabric

Pale-backed clothes moth
Monopis crocicapitella

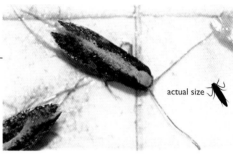

actual size

This moth has been recorded in birds' nests in Britain for many years, but is being found in houses in increasing numbers, particularly in London and south-east England.

It is similar in size to webbing clothes moth, but is very different in appearance: the adult is dark with a distinctive cream stripe down the back. The larvae live in silk bags similar to those of the case-bearing clothes moth, but they tend to carry the case at an angle. The pale-backed clothes moth is being noted more frequently in recent years because the males are attracted to the pheromone lure used in webbing clothes moth traps. There are recent records of the larvae attacking carpets and other wool textiles, but more information is needed to determine how much of a threat this moth will be to our clothes and furnishings.

Brown house moth
Hofmannophila pseudospretella

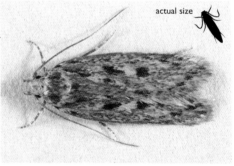

actual size

The brown house moth is larger than the clothes moths (10–12mm) and is coppery coloured with distinct dark patches on the wings. Larvae feed on organic debris and are common in birds' nests and blocked chimney flues. Although often found in houses, brown house moths are not a serious pest and only damage textiles undisturbed for long periods in damp conditions. Larvae sometimes feed on the glue of damp books, however, where they may make tunnels in the spines.

(Right) A leather-bound book eaten by brown house moth larvae

White-shouldered house moth
Endrosis sarcitrella

The white-shouldered house moth is very distinctive with a mottled grey appearance and a characteristic bright white patch of hairs on the head and shoulders. Like those of the brown house moth, the larvae feed on organic debris and are common in birds' nests and blocked chimney flues. Although commonly found in houses, white-shouldered house moths are not serious pests and will only cause damage to textiles when

actual size

they are undisturbed for long periods. They have been found living on fluff in central heating ducts in the summer and the adult moths get blown out into rooms when the heating is turned on in the autumn.

Indian meal moth
Plodia interpunctella

This moth is often confused with the clothes moth, but is much more strikingly patterned. Meal moths will not attack textiles, but are very serious pests of stored food worldwide and the larvae will attack cereals, dried seeds, nuts, chocolate and dried fruit. Indian meal moths are often found flying around in kitchens and food stores, from where they may fly into other rooms. The larvae live in the food and spin webbing similar to that produced by clothes moths. When they are fully grown they migrate from the food by chewing holes through packets and may be found crawling up walls or the insides of cupboards to pupate in a silk cocoon in cracks or crevices.

actual size

actual size

(Above) **Indian meal moth larva feeding on a nut in a bar of chocolate**

Prevention and control of moths

Clothes moths

The key to the control of both webbing and case-bearing clothes moths is good management and housekeeping. The adults fly around and are relatively easy to kill with insecticides, but they do not cause the damage. It is the larvae, hidden away in dark, undisturbed places, that eat textiles and are far more difficult to control.

Sticky traps with an attractant pheromone lure can be used to catch and detect adult moths. The pheromone, a chemical produced by the female moths, attracts the male moths, which fly onto the trap and get stuck. Although very effective, each lure is usually specific to one type of moth and will not attract other species. Because only adult male moths are trapped, however, and not the females, it is not an effective method of control.

Indian meal moth

Successful control of Indian meal moth relies on identifying the food source they are living in and disposing of the infested food. If moth larvae have migrated from the food, the pupal cases need to be removed with a stiff brush and vacuum. Spraying insecticide is rarely effective and usually not desirable in areas where food is handled or stored.

Prevention is by regularly checking for moth infestation and carrying out stock rotation. Sealed plastic containers protect dried food from egg-laying insects and will also contain any infestation and stop it spreading. Particular care should be taken when buying dry pet or bird food in bulk, as this can result in food being stored for long periods, allowing any larvae to develop into adult moths which then lay more eggs.

(Below) **Webbing clothes moths caught on a sticky pheromone trap**

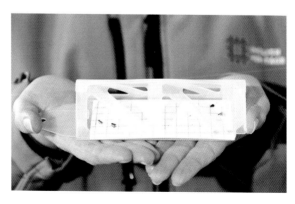

Key points for clothes moth prevention:

✓ **Regularly check and vacuum-clean wool carpets and rugs.** Pay particular attention to areas that are dark and undisturbed, such as under heavy furniture and at the edges of fitted carpets. Carpet inside fitted wardrobes and bathrooms is a particular favourite of moths and should also be regularly vacuum-cleaned or removed.

✓ **Regularly check wool clothing in drawers and wardrobes.** Look in folded textiles and in pockets and under lapels. Winter woollens are particularly susceptible to attack when they are put away for long periods in the warm summer months. If moths are detected, the affected items can be treated by freezing to kill all moths, larvae and eggs (see below and page 114) and then placed in sealed plastic storage boxes or bags until they are needed. Do not forget to also vacuum-clean the empty drawers and chests to remove any small larvae which may be hiding there.

✓ **Store fur and feather items carefully.** Old fur coats are especially vulnerable as, although they may never be worn, people are often reluctant to part with them and store them for years in a box. When the box is eventually opened the owners may be greeted by a cloud of moths and a lot of loose fur and damage. Moths will happily live on the feathers inside pillows and duvets, so these should be stored in sealed boxes or bags.

✓ **Avoid storing spare pieces of wool carpet.** Spare pieces of wool carpet, kept for years in cellars or attics, provide a safe, undisturbed environment and a source of food for moths which may then invade other parts of the house. Carpet rolls are particularly at risk, and may be extensively damaged. If you must keep them, store them in plastic sheeting.

✓ **Keep chimney flues clean and clear.** Blocked chimney flues are a major source of pest problems in many houses. If chimneys are unused and are not properly capped, large amounts of bird nest material can become trapped and provide food and harbourage for pests. Dead birds provide a protein bonus. Regular cleaning of flues is crucial, but it must also be linked to the fitting of caps on unused chimneys to prevent further debris dropping down. Removable grilles in fireplaces can also be fitted as long as they allow air to circulate through the flue.

Wool insulation. Natural wool insulation installed in attics and sometimes in cavity walls can also lead to clothes moth infestations. These warm, dark and undisturbed environments with abundant food, provide a perfect habitat for clothes moths. Although some types of insulation are treated to prevent moths developing, all such installations should be used with caution and very carefully monitored. Infested wool in attics can be replaced, but it is very difficult to treat or remove wool from cavity walls.

Taxidermy. Specimens in sealed cases are less vulnerable than those on open display, but may be attacked by moths. If stored, they should be wrapped in plastic sheeting. Note that some older taxidermy items are less vulnerable because arsenic was used in the preparation of the skins.

If items of clothing are found to be infested with moths, they should be wrapped in plastic and placed in a freezer at -20°C for at least two weeks. This will kill all eggs, larvae, pupae and adults. After treatment, the items can be cleaned carefully and then stored in plastic bags to prevent reinfestation. Vacuum-sealed storage bags are particularly useful as they occupy less space and are airtight. Rugs, carpets and other textiles can also be treated by deep freezing after being wrapped in plastic. Large carpets or other objects will need to be treated in a commercial freezer.

(Right) **Piles of folded woollen textiles left undisturbed for long periods are an ideal home for clothes moths**

CARPET BEETLES

There are two main types of carpet beetles: the small, round, ladybird-like varied carpet beetle *Anthrenus verbasci*; and the larger, oval, black two-spot carpet beetle *Attagenus pellio*, also known as the fur beetle. The natural home of carpet beetles is bird and animal nests and the carcases of dead animals. The feeding stage is the larva, which will eat almost anything made of animal protein. Particular favourites are fur, wool and feathers, but they will also eat horn and tortoiseshell. The adult beetles fly and the females lay eggs in or near the food source. The larvae are very small when they first hatch, but grow quickly when there is a good supply of food. As they grow, they moult and shed their skins, which often remain stuck to the material they are eating.

Recorded distribution of varied carpet beetle

(Below) **Wool jersey damaged by varied carpet beetle larvae**

Varied carpet beetle
Anthrenus verbasci

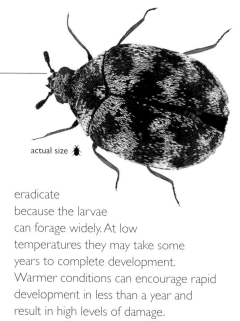

actual size

The most common species found in Britain is the varied carpet beetle, although there are a number of other species of *Anthrenus* which are similar in appearance and habits. All adult *Anthrenus* are small, round beetles, 2–3mm long and covered with black, grey and gold scales. Identification of the species is by the pattern and shape of these scales. Adult beetles fly well in warm weather and may frequently be found on windowsills. In Britain they are often found outside in late spring and early summer where they mate on flowers before returning indoors to lay batches of eggs secreted in cracks and crevices.

The eggs hatch into short, fat, hairy larvae which will eventually grow up to 5mm long and are often referred to as 'woolly bears'. When the larvae first hatch they are extremely small, less than 1mm long, and can gain entry to drawers and cupboards through very small cracks. As the larvae grow they leave empty, hairy cast skins, or moults, which may be the first signs of infestation. The larvae are voracious feeders and will rapidly demolish animal specimens, fur and feathers and woollen textiles. Clean cotton materials are not normally attacked. Carpet beetles are found in natural situations, such as birds' nests, and can find their way into our houses from old wasps' nests and birds' nests in attics and chimneys. Once established, they can be difficult to eradicate because the larvae can forage widely. At low temperatures they may take some years to complete development. Warmer conditions can encourage rapid development in less than a year and result in high levels of damage.

actual size

(Above) **Cast skins left by carpet beetle larvae when they moult**

Case study: Woolly bears at Down House

Charles Darwin lived in Down House, Kent, for over 40 years. In 1996 the house was taken into the care of English Heritage, when it was extensively refurbished.

The rooms were furnished to represent the house as lived in by Darwin and his family in the 19th century. This included fitting thick, red wool druggets in the downstairs rooms to recreate an important part of the original Victorian décor.

A pest monitoring programme using insect traps was put in place when the house was reopened to the public. A few months afterwards, small varied carpet beetle larvae were found on some of the traps. As the months went on more, larger 'woolly bear' larvae were found on the traps in rooms with the wool druggets. A detailed search revealed that the larvae were living in the druggets. They had eaten holes at the edges of the room where the drugget was turned under, providing a perfect habitat. Fortunately, the new wool drugget was more attractive to the pests than the older historical wool in the house and the infestation was spotted early on, before there was any insect damage to the historic carpets or upholstery. Remedial action was immediately carried out with thorough vacuuming of the druggets and targeted spraying with permethrin micro-emulsion (see page 118). It is not possible to entirely eradicate carpet beetles in a historic house such as Down, so the rooms are regularly vacuum-cleaned and monitored to ensure that numbers of carpet beetle larvae do not increase.

Key lessons:

✖ *The introduction of new wool into a house may increase the risk of textile pests: new wool is usually more attractive to pests than old wool.*

✖ *Although reproduction pure wool textiles may be historically authentic, it may be advisable to avoid these in historic house settings where an increase in the number of textile pests could jeopardise historic collections.*

(Top) Darwin's study at Down House, Kent, fitted with red wool drugget carpeting
(Right) Sticky trap used to catch carpet beetle larvae

Guernsey carpet beetle
Anthrenus sarnicus

actual size

The Guernsey carpet beetle, is slightly larger than the varied carpet beetle and is more greyish in appearance. It was introduced from Guernsey into London in 1971 and is now well established in south-east England. Guernsey carpet beetle causes damage similar to the varied carpet beetle, but prefers warmer conditions and will breed more quickly. It seems to be spreading across the British Isles and has been found as far north as Aberdeen.

Two-spot carpet or fur beetle
Attagenus pellio

actual size

The two-spot carpet, or fur, beetle is found in most historic houses in Britain, but is now less common in domestic houses. The black beetles are variable in size from 3–6mm and have a distinctive white spot on each wing case. They are active flyers and may be attracted to lights. The eggs hatch into larvae which are long and carrot-shaped with a tuft of bristles at the end of the body. They are much less spiky than the 'woolly bears' of varied carpet beetles because the hairs lie flat along the body. They are very small when first hatched and shed stripy skins as they feed and eventually grow to about 10mm long. Two-spot carpet beetles are common

actual size

in birds' nests and other animal debris and they are often found in the attics of old houses. They will damage fur, feathers and wool textiles.

Brown carpet beetle or 'vodka' beetle
Attagenus smirnovi

The brown carpet beetle, known as the 'vodka beetle', is a common pest in Europe and has now become established in London where it is a major domestic and museum pest. The adult beetle has a black head and thorax and brown wing cases and is covered with very fine hairs. The larvae appear similar to those of two-spot carpet beetle, but they are more active and seem to require some

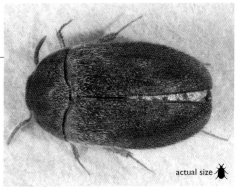

actual size

starch in their diet. Vodka beetles are often found in old organic debris under floorboards and other structural spaces.

Hide and leather beetles
Dermestes sp.

actual size

Hide or leather beetles are related to carpet beetles and, as their name suggests, will attack leather and skins. They will not, however, feed on tanned leather in good condition. There are a number of similar species which are all black, such as the Peruvian hide beetle *Dermestes peruvianus*, although the larder beetle, *Dermestes lardarius* (pictured here), has a distinctive pale band across the wing cases. The larder beetle was very common in kitchens and larders in the past and can still be found in historic houses. The very hairy larvae are dark brown or black and 15mm long when fully grown. Their natural home is animal carcasses, so

actual size

the presence of *Dermestes* adults and larvae in a house may be a sign that there is a dead rodent or bird hidden in a blocked chimney or structural void.

Prevention and control of carpet beetles

Signs of carpet beetle damage are usually small, neat holes bitten through fabric, or small cavities in carpet. Despite the name, carpet beetle larvae will eat clothes and anything made of wool, fur or feathers. The larvae produce a gritty excreta, known as frass, when they feed, which is often seen under damaged items. There will usually be small, hairy husks which are the skins shed by the larvae as they moult, but unlike moth damage, there will be no silk webbing.

Sticky traps can be used to catch adult beetles and are particularly useful for detecting the wandering larvae, which are secretive and may be very difficult to find.

Techniques for preventing carpet beetle infestation are largely the same as those for preventing clothes moths, as their larvae share similar food sources and favour similar environmental conditions.

(Below) **A carpet beetle larva, known as a 'woolly bear'**

Key points for carpet beetle prevention:

✓ **Regularly check and vacuum-clean wool carpets and rugs** particularly areas which are dark and undisturbed, such as under heavy furniture and at the edges of fitted carpets.

✓ **Regularly check wool clothing in drawers and wardrobes.** Look in folded textiles and in pockets and under lapels. Winter woollens are often attacked when put away in drawers in the warm summer months. Once insects have been removed, pest-free items (see below) should be stored in sealed plastic boxes or bags until they are needed. Vacuum-sealed storage bags are particularly useful as they occupy less space and prevent reinfestation.

✓ **Check and store felt items carefully.**
Carpet beetle larvae are particularly fond of wool felt and they will damage box linings and felt in pianos and other musical instruments. They will also sometimes damage book spines when the larvae eat the animal glue.

✓ **Store fur and feather items carefully.** Like clothes moth larvae, carpet beetle larvae will attack fur and feather items, and old furs, pillows and duvets should be stored in airtight boxes to avoid damage.

✓ **Avoid storing spare rolls of carpet.** Spare pieces of wool carpet or old rugs kept for years in cellars or attics provide an ideal environment and source of food for carpet beetles. The carpet itself may be extensively damaged and the beetles harboured there may then invade other parts of the house.

(Right) **Carpet beetles are particularly partial to wool felt. The felt pads on the paws of this teddy bear have been targeted and damaged by carpet beetle larvae**

✓ **Keep chimney flues clean and clear.** As for clothes moths, unswept and unused chimney flues full of material from birds' nests and perhaps even the carcases of dead birds, can provide an ideal habitat and food source for carpet beetle larvae and lead to an infestation. Chimneys must be regularly cleaned and properly capped to prevent debris from dropping down.

Taxidermy. Specimens may be attacked by carpet beetles. If stored, they should be wrapped in plastic sheeting. Note that some old taxidermy is less vulnerable because of the toxic chemicals used in the preparation of the skins.

Mounted insects. Decorative cases of butterflies and other insects are very vulnerable to attack by larvae of carpet beetles. Well-sealed airtight cases will prevent this.

Items of clothing found to be infested with carpet beetles should be wrapped in plastic and placed in a freezer at -20°C for at least two weeks. This will kill all eggs, larvae, pupae and adults. After treatment, the items can be cleaned carefully and then stored in plastic bags to prevent reinfestation. Rugs, carpets and other textiles can also be treated by deep freezing after being wrapped in plastic. Large carpets or other objects will need to be treated in a commercial freezer.

(Above) **An Atlas moth specimen severely damaged by carpet beetle larvae**

Books, taxidermy and cases of insect specimens can be treated by freezing (see page 114). Seek advice from a conservator before carrying out any treatment on valuable musical instruments infested with carpet beetle larvae.

WOOD-BORING INSECTS

Timber is vulnerable to attack by a wide variety of wood-boring insects at all stages from a standing tree to a rotting log. Some wood-boring species can be brought into homes with fresh logs for fires, but will not cause damage to dry, seasoned wood in houses or furniture. The main pests of seasoned timber, which present the greatest hazard to wooden objects and structural timber in houses, are the furniture beetle or woodworm *Anobium punctatum* and the deathwatch beetle *Xestobium rufovillosum*. Adult insects do not eat wood and cause few problems: it is the larvae that eat the timber and cause damage that may range from a few holes in a picture frame to the complete destruction of floorboards or roof beams.

People often panic when they find holes in furniture and structural timber, but these may have been caused by an ancient infestation that is no longer active. It is essential to distinguish between wood that contains active infestation of eggs, larvae or adults, and wood which has exit holes, but no longer contains any living larvae.

(Below) **Infested wood beam showing the smaller emergence holes of furniture beetles and the larger holes of deathwatch beetles**

Furniture beetle or woodworm
Anobium punctatum

The common furniture beetle or woodworm is widespread in houses in Britain where it can infest structural timber, furniture and wooden objects. The dark brown beetles are 3–5mm long with a characteristic hump in the thorax. The adult beetles emerge during the spring and early summer months by gnawing circular exit holes 1.5–2mm in diameter in the wood. As they fly or crawl away, wood dust and larval excreta (frass) may fall out of the hole. This leaves the characteristic sign of active beetle infestation – small piles of fresh bore dust. The frass feels gritty and is the shape of rice grains when seen under the microscope.

When the beetles have mated, the female lays eggs in crevices in the wood, particularly in end grain, unplaned timber or old exit holes. The eggs hatch in a few weeks and the larvae tunnel into the wood. As they gnaw and grow, the size of the tunnel increases. Wood is not very nutritious and so the larvae can take from two to five years to develop into adults, depending upon the type of wood and the conditions of temperature and moisture content.

Furniture beetle infestations will survive in cool, damp conditions, but do not thrive in dry conditions with humidity below 55%. This means that objects and structural wood in centrally heated buildings are very unlikely to support woodworm infestation. Outbreaks of woodworm activity are usually confined to outbuildings or areas that are damp due to leaks, condensation or poor air circulation. Adults will emerge from

Furniture beetle life cycle

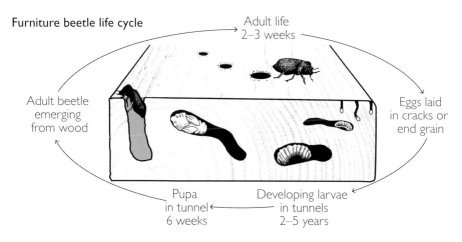

Adult life
2–3 weeks

Adult beetle emerging from wood

Eggs laid in cracks or end grain

Pupa in tunnel 6 weeks

Developing larvae in tunnels 2–5 years

infested wood which is moved from damper to drier conditions, but the eggs and young larvae will not survive.

Anobium larvae will attack most wood except sound heartwood, but they prefer starchy hardwood and softwood. Plywood from the first half of the 20th century is particularly susceptible, because of the added protein from casein and blood albumen, and it can be severely damaged. Woodworm larvae will even develop in books and wood pulp paper when the leaves are compressed, which is why the larvae are sometimes called 'bookworms'. They will rarely attack clean, dry books, although an attack may spread from infested wooden shelving.

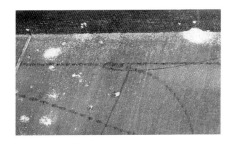

(Top right) Piles of frass from fresh furniture beetle emergence holes
(Above right) Furniture beetle emergence holes in infested sapwood. The adjacent darker-coloured heartwood is not damaged

Korynetes caeruleus

Shiny metallic blue beetles about 5mm long are sometimes found in old houses. These beetles, called *Korynetes*, and their larvae are active predators of the larvae of furniture beetles and other wood-borers. Although these helpful insects are not pests, they indicate the presence of a substantial wood-boring beetle infestation, which should be investigated.

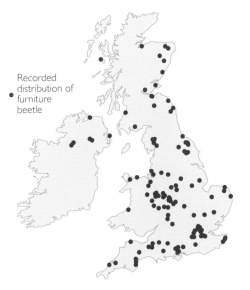

Recorded distribution of furniture beetle

actual size

Case study: Furniture beetles at Deal Castle

In the summer of 2013, adult furniture beetles and frass were found by site staff underneath the seat pads of some of the wooden chairs in the Captain's Flat in Deal Castle, Kent.

An investigation revealed old and new beetle emergence holes in the seat pad frames. The room and its contents were checked for other signs of furniture beetle activity and, in addition to the chairs, some of the floorboards, a wooden wardrobe and a large picture frame were found to have signs of emergence. The room and its contents were thoroughly cleaned and the chairs were placed onto a large piece of white sheeting so that staff could monitor for further signs of emerging beetles and frass during the summer months. Staff regularly checked the chairs and the sheeting and a few more dead furniture beetles and frass were found.

As the wooden chairs were not part of Deal Castle's collection of historic objects, we decided to dispose of the infested seat pads and replace them. All the other wooden items, including the floorboards in the room, were treated with a permethrin micro-emulsion spray (see page 118) in situ as a precaution to prevent further spread of active furniture beetle infestation.

Since then, the objects in the room have been regularly checked and, after two years, no more signs of infestation have been evident. It is now only necessary to carry out good housekeeping measures and regular visual checks during the spring and summer months.

Key lessons:

✓ *Identify the source of a furniture beetle infestation and establish which objects are actively infested.*

✓ *Checking every year for new beetle activity will determine whether an infestation has been successfully eliminated.*

(Above right) Fresh furniture beetle emergence holes in the seat frame of one of the chairs
(Right) Infested chairs standing on white sheeting to show up frass from fresh beetle emergence

Deathwatch beetle
Xestobium rufovillosum

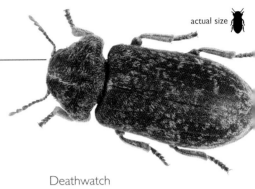

actual size

The deathwatch beetle is one of the most well-known and feared pests of timber. It is unlikely, however, to cause problems in most houses as it will only live in the sorts of old timbers found in historic buildings. In warm weather between March and June adult male beetles make tapping noises to attract a mate, and it is from this sound that the name 'deathwatch beetle' derives. The clicking sounds could easily be heard in the quiet of the night and the sound became associated with night-time vigils for the dead or dying.

Deathwatch beetle larvae attack hardwoods, particularly oak and elm, and softwood is usually only attacked when it is in direct contact with infested hardwood. Damage to old timber can be very severe and result in total failure of load-bearing beams. The adults are brown with a scattering of small yellow

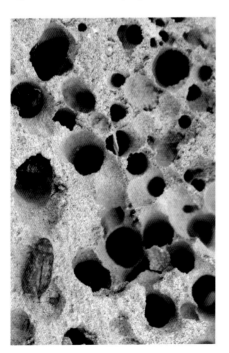

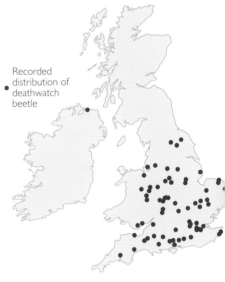

Recorded distribution of deathwatch beetle

(Above) **The low incidence of deathwatch beetle in Scotland is due to the fact that oak is rare and not often used in buildings**
(Left) **Deathwatch beetle tunnels in oak**

Case study: Deathwatch beetles at Audley End House

In 1997 Audley End House, Essex, became the first property in which English Heritage carried out an integrated pest management trapping programme.

During an initial assessment to decide where to place pest traps, a number of deathwatch beetles were found on the floor immediately under a hatch leading to the North Tower. It was clear that they had fallen from a damaged area of ceiling around the hatch. After the area was repaired to stop damp ingress, the numbers of new adults emerging fell every year.

In 2002, however, about 20 beetles were found on the floor of the great hall, most near a bay window. This pointed to a problem in the roof above the window and a survey was carried out. Although it seemed sound and uninfested, house staff recalled that, six years previously,

(Above) **The damp wood around this roof hatch at Audley End House was infested by deathwatch beetles**

a downpipe in the area had become blocked and the overflowing rain gully had soaked the timber of the roof nearby. Emergence of beetles in 2002 was consistent with the very long life cycle of deathwatch beetles: adult beetles from eggs laid in the damp timbers in 1996 had emerged long after the problem had been rectified. No remedial action was necessary and numbers of emerging beetles have dropped over the years.

In 2004 deathwatch beetles were found in two second-floor store rooms. Investigations revealed damp, infested timber behind the plaster. Remedial work was carried out to stop damp ingress and the number of adult beetles emerging has declined since then. In the same year, deathwatch beetle damage was noticed in floor joists of the Little Drawing Room. An insect trap was placed in the floor void, which caught three deathwatch beetles. Only a few adult beetles were found in the area until 2016 when over 20 were found on the floor. Investigation of the floor void showed evidence of active infestation with fresh piles of frass and new emergence holes. Although there were no obvious signs of damp, ventilation was improved and the area is now being closely monitored with regular moisture recordings.

Key lessons:

✓ *Low levels of deathwatch beetle infestation are to be expected in very old buildings with oak timbers. It is important, however, not to allow them to increase in numbers.*

✓ *An understanding of the beetle's life cycle and its reliance on timber that has been exposed to high moisture levels will help determine what action, if any, needs to be taken.*

✓ *Regular maintenance of buildings to prevent water ingress and damp, as well as visual inspections to check for beetles and signs of their activity can prevent an infestation from becoming established.*

scales and are quite large (6–9mm). The larvae take five to ten years to develop and adult exit holes are larger than woodworm exit holes, at up to 3mm in diameter. The frass from infested timber is in the form of coarse, round pellets.

Deathwatch beetle larvae will only develop in timber that has been damp and previously attacked by fungus. This means that many old houses and buildings with oak timbers may have low levels of infestation in damper areas. Small numbers of beetles each year should not cause a problem. It is important, however, to be vigilant for signs of increased local attack, which may be connected to damp ingress some years earlier. Extensive infestation can be very localised in damp areas and timbers can be hollowed out by the larvae. If there is beetle activity in the bearing ends of roof beams which are in contact with damp walls, it is usually advisable to get expert guidance to avoid structural failure.

Powder post beetle
Lyctus brunneus

actual size

This wood-borer is very different from deathwatch beetle and furniture beetle. Established infestations are rare in Britain, but *Lyctus* powder post beetles are often introduced in wood and furniture from warmer countries. A number of different species have been recorded, but *Lyctus brunneus* seems to be the most common. Adult insects have been known to emerge from new woodblock flooring six months to a year after it has been installed. They have also been found emerging from furniture and picture frame mouldings imported from southern Europe. Fortunately, powder post beetles will usually only attack relatively fresh wood with a high starch and sugar content. This means that older wooden objects and structural timbers with a low starch content, such as oak heartwood, are not at risk.

Infestation by powder post beetle can easily be recognised by the characteristic very fine, talc-like, powdery frass which falls from larval tunnels and exit holes. The larvae develop in deciduous hardwoods such as oak, tropical hardwoods and bamboo. In warm conditions, after about one year's development, the adult beetles emerge leaving exit holes 1.5–2mm in diameter. The adults are 5–6mm long, flat, reddish-brown beetles. Severe infestations will reduce wood to a powdery mass surrounded by a paper-thin shell.

Case study: Powder post beetles at Dover Castle

In the summer of 2012, two dead beetles were found next to a reproduction oak barrel stand in the kitchen area of the great tower at Dover Castle, Kent. They were not furniture beetles, as might have been expected, but were identified as powder post beetle, *Lyctus brunneus*.

Most of the recently installed reproduction furniture had come from the same supplier and had been made from new, untreated and unfinished wood. Powder post beetles need wood with a high starch content and will not feed or breed in old wood as it does not provide sufficient nutrients.

In Britain, powder post beetles tend to emerge only once a year and so, as a precaution, a decision was taken to treat the stand regularly with an insecticidal water-based permethrin micro-emulsion spray to kill any emerging beetles. A close watch was kept on all the wooden props displayed in the room to see if any more beetles appeared, indicating a major infestation. Temperature measurements were also regularly taken on each floor of the tower to see if differences might explain why we had not seen any signs of emergence from other wooden items. By February 2013, the barrel stand was still the only object affected, and the decision was taken to dispose of it. A new stand was commissioned using heat-treated wood. The barrels showed no signs of infestation and were not replaced, but were treated with permethrin spray as a precaution and have been closely monitored. Since then, no signs of emergence or fresh powder post beetles have been found.

Key lessons:

✓ *Accurate identification of insects is vital in determining the correct course of treatment and monitoring.*

✓ *Being patient and waiting to see if there are further signs of activity can help to avoid carrying out expensive and unnecessary remedial treatments.*

(Top) The kitchen area of the great tower, with reproduction wood furniture
(Right) Emergence holes of adult powder post beetles

Prevention and control of wood-boring beetles

If objects or timber show signs of wood-borer damage it is essential to determine if the infestation is active and, if so, how widespread. This can be difficult and requires planning and patience, but it is much better to wait a few months to gather information than spend time, money and effort on unnecessary chemical treatments. Infestation of woodworm or deathwatch beetle in furniture or other objects requires a different approach to infestation in structural timber.

(Below) **An oak roof beam destroyed by the tunnelling of deathwatch beetles**

Key points for movable objects and furniture:

✓ **Determine whether an infestation is active.** Objects suspected of being infested with furniture beetles should be brushed or vacuum-cleaned to remove dust and then isolated and checked regularly from March to June. If there are no new emergence holes or signs of fresh bore dust after this time, then it is unlikely there is any active infestation and no action will need to be taken.

✓ **Control moisture levels.** In a dry environment, active infestation of furniture and other wooden objects is unlikely in objects which have been there for some years. Newly acquired items, however, such as furniture or picture frames, may have been kept in damper conditions which encourage furniture beetle. There have been frequent cases of people buying objects at sale rooms and then being surprised the following spring by lots of new holes, piles of bore dust and furniture beetles on the floor. For these objects, it is likely that the infestation will die out as the wood dries, although this may take a few years.

If treatment is required, small objects can be wrapped in polythene and placed in a freezer at -20°C for at least three weeks. Larger objects may need to be treated in a commercial freezer or controlled humidity heat chamber.

Key points for structural timbers:

✓ **Determine whether an infestation is active and how extensive it is.** Infestation of furniture beetle in timber panelling, floorboards and roof beams can be worrying, but it is essential to know where and how extensive the activity is. Similarly, houses with old oak beams will probably have a small number of deathwatch beetle emergence holes. A few beetles emerging each year will not be a risk to the structure and some people regard this as an acceptable part of owning a historic property.

(Right) **A pile of frass indicates the fresh emergence of a deathwatch beetle from the beam above**

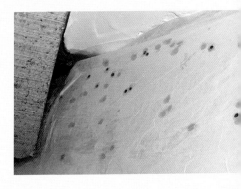

(Right) Tissue paper pasted onto a beam infested by deathwatch beetle. Here, the blue marks indicate new holes; the pink and orange marks are holes from previous years

A good way to check for active infestation by both furniture beetles and deathwatch beetles is to paste tissue paper over areas of wood with emergence holes and record new holes in the paper the following spring. A decline in emergence each year will show that the problem is dying away. If numbers increase in particular areas, however, this may be a warning that there are underlying structural problems which need to be rectified.

✓ **Monitor and control moisture in timbers.** Damp is the key to active infestation by both furniture beetle and deathwatch beetle and structural surveys can help to pinpoint areas of water ingress or poor air circulation. It is a waste of time to carry out any chemical treatments unless damp problems are rectified. Simply unblocking air bricks and mending leaking gutters often allows timber to dry out, resulting in an infestation gradually dying out without any need for treatment.

Determining which areas are at risk requires patience and understanding and it may be necessary to engage an expert surveyor. Because of the long life cycle of deathwatch beetles, emergence of adults may occur up to ten years after any water ingress. Always ensure that any structural survey includes extensive measurement of timber moisture content to produce a map of high risk areas, which can be monitored more closely.

In some cases it is not possible to maintain lower moisture levels and some pesticide treatment may therefore be needed. An insecticide treatment on its own, however, is rarely effective against either furniture beetle or deathwatch beetle infestation. The chemicals may kill emerging adults, but the damaging larvae are hidden deep in the wood where the insecticide does not penetrate. If the problem is serious then it may be necessary to call in specialist advice.

Infestation by powder post beetles is usually confined to new starchy wood and does not spread to old timber. Unlike deathwatch beetles and furniture beetles, however, they will not die out in low humidity, so infested flooring or structural wood may need to be replaced. Infested furniture and other objects can be treated by freezing or controlled humidity heat treatment (see pages 114–15).

DAMP-LOVING PESTS

Many insects live in damp outdoor environments and if you disturb leaf litter or compost, or look under stones or bark, you will often see small creatures scurrying away. Most of these play a very important role in the cycle of decay which returns nutrients to the soil. A few, such as silverfish, fungus beetles and booklice, are also able to survive indoors in human environments, but only if the conditions are moist enough. If you find them in your house it is probably a sign, therefore, that there are localised damp areas.

(Below) **A common silverfish (*Lepisma saccharina*) in its natural habitat**

Relative humidity

There are many terms to describe the amount of water in the air and one of the most commonly used is 'relative humidity', often abbreviated to RH.

The relationship of air and water is complex, however, and often misunderstood. The extremes are saturated air, which is 100% RH and cannot hold any more water, and dry air, which is 0% RH and has no water in it. Cold air can only carry a fraction of the water that can be carried by warm air. A classic illustration of this effect can be seen in a hot shower: the air inside the shower is warm and can carry a lot of water, but as soon as the air comes into contact with a cold tile wall, window or mirror, it cools rapidly and loses its capacity to carry as much water. This results in condensation, with water running down the surfaces.

High humidity above 75% may encourage silverfish, furniture beetles and mould. Central heating will generally create a low relative humidity which may deter some pests, but can cause objects to dry out. This may result in damage to sensitive objects, such as pianos and other musical instruments. When warm air in houses comes into contact with colder areas, such as water pipes or north-facing walls, it loses its capacity to hold as much water and may result in local condensation and localised pest problems and mould growth.

The key to preventing problems caused by relative humidity is a question of balance. If possible, keep conditions broadly between 40 to 60% RH and avoid extremes of temperature. If you suspect there may be problems with high humidity, there are simple low-cost digital humidity meters which can provide accurate measurements to identify problem areas.

(Above right) **This book, stored in a damp cellar, has been damaged by mould and silverfish. The humidity meter shows a high local relative humidity of 75.5%**
(Right) **Mould growing inside a damp cupboard resulting from poor air circulation**

Silverfish

Silverfish are members of a group of organisms called bristletails which have been on Earth for over 200 million years. Although they are primitive insects, they are very successful across the world. Silverfish are usually associated with damp conditions and generally require localised relative humidity above 75–80% to breed and multiply.

Unlike beetles and moths, juvenile silverfish are nymphs that look like miniature adults. They moult a number of times as they grow and may take a year to reach adulthood. Adults are silver, segmented, scaly and wingless with long antennae and three long forked bristles at the tail end. Adults are between 10 and 15mm long. Silverfish are general scavengers and feed on starch, animal glue, organic material and microscopic moulds on paper. The most common species, *Lepisma saccharina* (pictured above), will damage wallpaper, books, prints, labels, postage stamps and paper currency. Silverfish will also

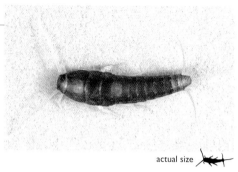

actual size

(Top) **Common silverfish *Lepisma saccharina*** *(Above)* **Paper grazed and damaged by silverfish**

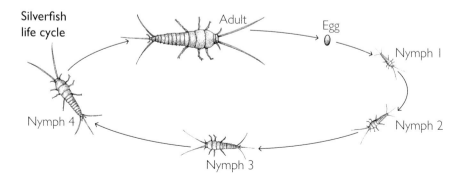

Silverfish life cycle

Adult
Egg
Nymph 1
Nymph 2
Nymph 3
Nymph 4

damage photographs when they eat the gelatin layer. Damage is caused by the insect scraping the surface of what they are eating causing eroded areas of thinned and weakened paper which will eventually break through to make holes.

Silverfish are useful indicators of damp problems and if found in high numbers in an apparently dry room, it is likely that there are high humidity micro-environments nearby. They are frequently found in kitchens and bathrooms, for example, where they may live in the damper areas behind skirting boards, under vinyl and lino flooring and underneath sealed-in baths. Wallpaper is particularly vulnerable if starch wallpaper paste has been used. Silverfish may live in cracks and crevices around wood beams and emerge at night to graze and feed on the surrounding wallpaper.

Firebrats, *Thermobia domestica*, are very similar in appearance to silverfish, but are cream with brown speckles rather than silver. They cause

(Above) **Wallpaper grazed and damaged by silverfish living in a damp crevice next to a roof beam**

similar damage to paper, but are not as common as silverfish and prefer warmer conditions. Another species of silverfish, the grey silverfish (*Ctenolepisma longicaudata*), is starting to be recorded in Britain (see page 89).

Feasting on ink

Silverfish have been known to cause considerable damage to handwritten paper and card museum labels when stored in damper conditions. They scrape the surface of the paper to eat older inks made with fungal and vegetable-based ingredients, rendering handwritten labels unreadable and leaving objects without information about where or when they were found.

Cig___tte ___ made by an Italian prisoner of War in India from a mess Tin.

Booklice

Booklice are sometimes called bark lice, which gives an indication of one of their natural habitats. There are a number of different species which will live in houses, although *Liposcelis bostrychophila* is the most common in heated buildings. The adults are wingless and very small, less than 1mm long. They develop through a series of nymphal stages that feed on organic material and microscopic moulds on a range of substrates including flour, paper and cardboard. They are parthenogenic, meaning that there are no males and the females do not require fertilisation to lay eggs. As a result, populations of booklice can increase very rapidly at temperatures above 25°C giving rise to apparent population explosions.

actual size ➤

(Above) **Adults and nymphs of the common booklouse *Liposcelis bostrychophila***

Booklice have appeared in very large numbers in new or recently refurbished houses where straw board has been used in walls and partitions. The straw used in the board contains enough residual fungal growth for booklice to feed upon, allowing them to breed rapidly and then emerge from gaps around doors and light fittings. Although they will eventually die out as the fungus in the straw board disappears, this may take some years and treatment is very difficult. There have also been similar problems in so-called 'eco-houses' made with straw bales. Booklice can also be found living in unsealed packets of flour, cereals and baby formula milk powder.

Although direct damage may not be as serious as that caused by silverfish, large numbers of booklice will scrape the surface of books and papers. In addition, squashed bodies will stain paper and may encourage moulds.

While many booklice thrive in conditions of high humidity, which encourages mould growth, *Liposcelis* can tolerate drier conditions than some other booklice and can cause infestations when the relative humidity is as low as 60%. Booklice can be a particular problem of books and manuscripts, but they will not be at risk if kept in clean, dry, cool conditions.

The black booklouse, *Lepinotus patruelis*, is found in cooler, damper conditions, but rarely in sufficient numbers to cause damage. The presence on traps of small, red-brown pseudoscorpions, a type of arachnid that eats booklice, often indicates a booklouse infestation. Winged booklice are sometimes found in large numbers on windowsills and pest traps. They have usually come in from outside and will not survive for long indoors.

(Right) **Pseudoscorpion, a predator of booklice**
(Below) **Adults and nymphs of black booklouse**

actual size ▼

Fungus beetles and plaster beetles

There are many species of very small beetles, 1–3mm long, which live outdoors on decaying material and eat moulds and fungi. Some are able to survive in houses, usually where there are very damp conditions. Plaster beetles are often found in large numbers in buildings which have recently been refurbished and replastered. As the building dries out, they usually decrease in numbers and then disappear as the source of fungal food is used up.

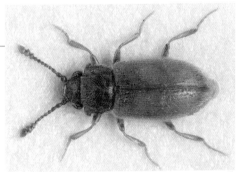

actual size ✳

(Above right) **Fungus beetle *Cryptophagus* species**
(Right) **Plaster beetle *Adistemia* species**

actual size ✳

Persistent infestations of fungus beetles or plaster beetles indicate a continuing damp problem, caused by leaks, condensation or poor air circulation.

Small numbers are not a cause for concern, but the presence of large numbers of beetles indicates an incipient damp problem with fungal growth.

Wood weevils

Although many beetles are sometimes referred to as 'weevils', wood weevils, *Euophryum confine* and *Pentarthrum huttoni*, are a member of a group called the 'true weevils'. They are characterised by a long snout with jaws on the end that enable them to bore into hard objects. Many weevils are pests of cereal grains and nuts, but wood weevils, which are small, slender and black with a long snout, are specialised in eating wood. They are not major pests as they only eat wood that is really damp. They are, however, useful indicators of damp problems and have been found, for

actual size 🐜

example, eating the edges of woodblock flooring which has been subject to damp ingress through the walls and floor. Wood weevils have also been found in bathrooms eating damp wood hidden under lino.

(Above) **Wood weevil *Euophryum confine***
(Below) **Wooden brush head damaged by wood weevils**

Prevention and control of damp-loving pests

Silverfish, booklice and other damp-loving insects thrive when there is moisture in their environment. Damp wood, paper and plaster will encourage infestations.

Key points for damp-loving pest prevention:

✓ **Eliminate and control damp conditions.**
Common sources of additional moisture in houses are condensation, poor air circulation and damp penetration through walls and floors. Other causes may be leaking roofs, gutters and downpipes. In most cases, discovery and elimination of the source of moisture leads to a rapid decline in the insect population without the need for any extensive insecticide treatment. Local treatments will relieve immediate symptoms, but are not likely to cure the problem.

✓ **Leave air gaps behind books and objects against exterior walls.** Air gaps allow the circulation of air and help to prevent dampness and condensation.

✓ **Keep air bricks unblocked in older buildings.** It is vital to keep air bricks clear to allow free circulation of air.

(Top) **Poorly maintained waste pipes and gutters can cause significant damp issues leading to infestations by damp-loving pests**
(Right) **Air bricks should be kept clear to allow air to circulate**

Detritus Feeders and Scavengers

There are many species of beetle found in houses that are not serious pests, but which can occasionally cause nuisance or even serious damage if populations are able to build up.

Spider beetles

Spider beetles are so-named because they are superficially spider-like and although they only have six legs, their long antennae can be mistaken for a fourth pair of legs. Spider beetles are common in older houses where they live in birds' nests and organic debris in attics, chimney flues and cellars. They feed on a wide range of vegetable and animal detritus and will thrive on dried human or pet food. They will also feed on dead insects, and dead cluster flies (see page 65) may provide a good food source if they are not removed regularly.

There are many species, but the adults are usually hairy and generally slow-moving and breed slowly. The Australian spider beetle, *Ptinus tectus*, is 3–5mm long with a dull brown, hairy body and is common in many cooler countries around the world (pictured top). It is easily distinguished from the golden spider beetle, *Niptus hololeucus*, (pictured right) which is slightly larger and has a

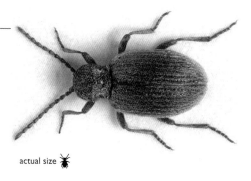

actual size

(Above) Australian spider beetle *Ptinus tectus*
(Below) Golden spider beetle *Niptus hololeucus*

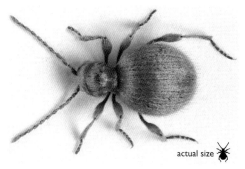

actual size

round body covered in shiny golden hairs. This species is becoming more common in historic houses where it often lives in disused chimney flues.

Another species being found more frequently is the white-marked spider beetle, *Ptinus fur.* This is so-called because it has small, indistinct white marks on the body. The males are lighter brown and thinner than the darker, rounded females.

All spider beetle larvae are similar in appearance, but are rarely seen because they tunnel into food. When they are fully grown, they chew a cavity and pupate inside a globular silk cocoon. This habit can lead to damaged books, paper and even wood shelving. Spider beetles are difficult to kill and will tolerate lower temperatures than many other beetles.

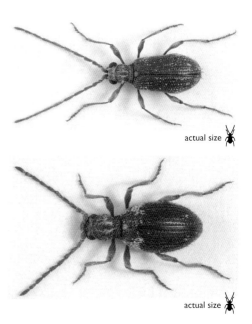

actual size

actual size

(Above) **White-marked spider beetle *Ptinus fur*: male (top) and female (bottom)**

Mealworm
Tenebrio molitor

Mealworms get their name from their large, leathery, yellowish larvae which live in old organic detritus, such as birds' nests. They are well known to fishermen, who use them as bait, and to bird-lovers who feed dried mealworms to birds.

actual size

(Above) **Adult and larvae of mealworm**

The adults are large (10–15mm long), black, slow-moving beetles, often found wandering around in attics and upstairs rooms. Although they used to be pests in old flour mills, they do not cause any damage to objects in houses. Mealworms usually indicate that there are birds' nests and other debris in attics or disused chimney flues. They are sometimes confused with black ground beetles which are active outdoor predators usually found near doors on the ground floor (see page 70).

Biscuit beetle or drugstore beetle
Stegobium paniceum

actual size 🐛

The biscuit beetle or drugstore beetle is a worldwide pest, particularly in warmer countries. It belongs to the same family as the common furniture beetle or woodworm, *Anobium punctatum*, but unlike woodworm larvae, which eat wood and cellulose, those of the biscuit beetle bore into hard, dried vegetable material including biscuits, nuts and dried plants. Adults are reddish-brown and 2–3mm long and when it is warm they are very active and will fly towards lights. The larvae are white and curved and will tunnel through hard materials. The beetles emerge from exit holes which are very like furniture beetle holes.

Case study: Biscuit beetles at Kenwood House

In 2011, biscuit beetles were regularly being found on sticky traps in the service wing store rooms at Kenwood House, London.

All the other rooms in the service wing were checked for beetles, but the pests seemed to be concentrated in these store rooms and their source was not identified. In the winter of 2012 the main roof voids above the store rooms were opened to carry out major repair works and a large number of old wasps' nests infested with biscuit beetles were found throughout the roof area. The nests were all professionally removed and disposed of before spring 2013 to deter any new queens from building new nests and to remove a potential food source for biscuit beetles and other pests.

Once the major roof works commenced, proofing was also installed to stop flying insects from gaining access to the roof spaces in the future. Since then, no more biscuit beetles have been found at Kenwood.

Key lessons:

✓ *Remove old wasps' nests to eliminate them as sources of food for pests.*

✓ *Make it difficult for new insects to gain access.*

(Above) Wasp nest infested with biscuit beetles

'Worm castles'

Biscuit beetles were called 'weevils' by Royal Navy sailors in the 18th and 19th centuries when the beetles infested their hard, dry ship's biscuits made of flour and water. The sailors banged the biscuits on the table to knock out the 'maggots' (larvae) and adult beetles before eating them. In the American Civil War, soldiers called these hardtack biscuits 'worm castles'.

The emerging adults can bore through hard materials, including foil, cardboard food boxes and plastic food containers. Development time from egg to adult depends upon food and temperature; in nutritious food at 30°C, it can be as short as five to six weeks. At lower temperatures, the life cycle may take up to a year and biscuit beetles will not survive out of doors in Britain.

Biscuit beetles have an amazing ability to survive and breed on dried plant material and spices, some of which are toxic to other animals. Infestations have been recorded in a wide variety of materials including cereals, biscuits, dried bread, pasta, chocolate, dog food, stock cubes, curry powder, cumin seed and cannabis. A large number of biscuit beetles can emerge from a relatively small food source. Hundreds of beetles were found, for example, in one building where they had been breeding on wheat grains being used as mouse bait in trays. There have been many cases of people mistaking an infestation of biscuit beetles for furniture beetles. This is a very good example of the need for accurate identification of insects: incorrectly identifying biscuit beetles as furniture beetles could lead to expensive and totally unnecessary insecticide treatment of wood.

(Above) **A hardtack biscuit of the American Civil War, dating from between 1861 and 1865. The holes made by biscuit beetles can still be seen**
(Below) **Dried food infested with biscuit beetles**

Prevention and control of detritus feeders and scavengers

Spider beetles and mealworms are often found in birds' nests, but will also thrive on dried human and pet food. Identifying their food source is key to preventing and controlling infestations. Other beetles such as flour beetles (*Tribolium* sp.) and grain beetles (*Oryzaephilus* sp.) may be found living in stored flour and cereals.

Key points for prevention of detritus feeders and scavengers:

✓ **Regularly remove organic debris.** An infestation of spider beetles or mealworms can be prevented by eliminating their food source and harbourage. They are less common in modern, centrally heated houses. In older properties, regular cleaning and removal of bird nests, dead cluster flies and other organic debris from loft spaces and chimney flues will usually keep numbers to a very low level.

✓ **Store dried food in airtight containers.** Infestations by biscuit beetles can be avoided by regularly checking stores of dried food, storing organic material in insect-proof containers and carrying out good stock rotation.

(Left) **A dead bird infested with insect pests in a neglected attic**

Flies

There are a vast number of different species of flies, with a wide variety of different life cycles and food sources. Depending upon the species, a fly buzzing around your house may have come from a number of different sources. Most adult flies will only feed on liquids, but the larval growing stages live in a range of materials. Blowflies, bluebottles and greenbottles emerge from larvae which have been living in meat, fish or carnivore excreta. Housefly larvae live in rotting vegetable material, but can also live in poultry and pig manure – a particular problem for people who live near pig or poultry farms where very large numbers of these flies can invade homes and cause great distress. Flies are not merely irritating, however, but can also pose a health hazard as they may land on exposed food or food preparation surfaces and transfer harmful bacteria.

(Below) **Adult flies on raw meat**

'Maggot therapy'

Maggots have been used to clean infected wounds since Roman times. There is renewed interest in the use of so-called 'maggot therapy' today, using sterile blowfly larvae, particularly of the common greenbottle fly, to remove necrotic tissue from persistent ulcers and other wounds. The maggots eat away dead flesh, leaving only healthy flesh, and there is evidence that their secretions promote healing and have an antibacterial effect.

Cluster fly
Pollenia rudis

actual size

Cluster flies, particularly *Pollenia rudis*, can be a problem and a great nuisance in many houses. The adults look like houseflies with golden hairs on the thorax and sometimes come into houses in their thousands to hibernate in the autumn, invading attics and upstairs rooms. Many of them die and the dead bodies provide an ideal source of food for carpet beetles and spider beetles. They love warm, sunny, south-facing walls and it is difficult to prevent the flies getting in as they are very persistent and will find small gaps and crevices. Sash windows seem particularly attractive and are difficult to proof. Flies also accumulate in window radiator boxes where they may be difficult to remove.

When the heating has been turned on and the house is warmer, the flies think it is spring and start to move around. They often fly to windows and accumulate in large numbers. *Pollenia* cluster flies have an unusual life cycle: the larvae are parasites of earthworms. This means that they are very common in rural areas with a lot of grassland. Historic houses with large

areas of grassy parkland are particularly attractive and the houses act like magnets in the autumn. In many cases flies return to the same place every year despite the fact that they represent a completely new generation. It is possible that large numbers of hibernating flies leave an attractant aggregation pheromone which attracts flies the following year.

(Right) **Cluster flies swarming on a window**

Fruit flies

Another type of fly commonly seen in houses is a very small gnat-like fly (*Drosophila* sp.) which can sometimes be found in very large numbers, particularly in kitchens. These flies are variously called vinegar flies, fruit flies, drain flies or bar flies. The larvae live in semi-liquid fermenting vegetable matter, such as decaying fruit, and may also be found where beer and fruit-based drinks are spilt. They can be a nuisance, and may spread bacteria. Removing their food source will usually eradicate an infestation.

Prevention and control of flies

Most aerosol insecticides are effective against adult flies and will knock them down and kill them rapidly. It is very important to remove the dead flies as soon as possible otherwise they will provide food for carpet beetles and spider beetles.

Ultraviolet attractant fly killer units can be very effective if they are installed and serviced correctly. The types which use a sticky board to catch flies are generally more suitable for domestic use than those with an electric killer grid. Catch trays from ultraviolet traps should be emptied regularly, as accumulations of dead flies will attract and feed carpet beetle larvae. For cluster flies, there are specific fly traps which can be attached to windows, and fresh lavender placed around windows may have a deterrent effect. Sponging down windows and sills with a damp cloth, once a year, may also help reduce numbers.

(Right) Dried lavender and a lavender sachet placed on a windowsill to repel cluster flies

Key points for prevention of flies:

✓ **Look for and remove dead birds or rodents.** Blowflies may be an indicator that there is a dead bird or rodent nearby. If the flies are only appearing in a closed room with a fireplace, then it is almost certain there is a carcase in the chimney flue.

✓ **Use rubbish bins with tight-fitting lids.** Houseflies may be coming from rubbish bins.

✓ **Keep drains unblocked.** Fruit flies may be from compost or a blocked drain.

✓ **Stop flies from getting in.** Fly screens can stop flies from entering through doors and windows. Make sure windows are tight-fitting to prevent flies from squeezing through gaps.

✓ Do not leave food exposed.

(Below) **Cluster flies can aggregate in their thousands, as in this extreme example. Dead flies can attract other pests and should be removed**

OTHER INVERTEBRATE INVADERS

Some species of insects and other invertebrates invade our homes accidentally, such as night-flying moths attracted to indoor lights, and creatures that creep under doors and then cannot find their way back outside. Others, such as ladybirds and lacewings, may be looking for a warm, dry place to hibernate during the winter. In the summer months, ants may be a nuisance as they come into our homes to look for additional food sources.

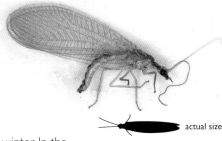

actual size

(Above) Adult lacewing

Ants

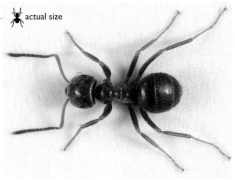

actual size

Some species of ants may invade houses at certain times of the year. The workers of the black garden ant *Lasius niger* (pictured here) often nest under paths and patios near houses and will leave their outside colonies to forage inside buildings for food. They particularly like sweet food, such as sugar and honey, and although they can be very annoying, they will cause little damage. Ant colonies produce very large numbers of flying ants in the summer and these may cause great nuisance if they get into buildings. This phase does not last long, however, and after a few days the flying ants should disappear. In the past, worker ant invasions were usually restricted to the summer months, but there have been recent cases where ants living under

floors have been found wandering around houses in the winter months.

The brown garden ant *Lasius brunneus,* which is found mainly in south-east England, can create nests by tunnelling in soft and rotting timber. It has also been found causing serious damage to cork and polystyrene insulation. Another species *Lasius neglectus*, which is quite difficult to distinguish from the native black garden ant, has recently been found in Britain for the first time. It is common in Europe and can invade houses in large numbers and cause serious problems.

In urban areas, problems can be caused by invasive tropical species, such as pharaoh's ant, *Monomorium pharaonis*. This very small ant is a serious pest in hospitals and restaurants and will sometimes colonise adjacent houses. Control and eradication of pharaoh's ants and other introduced species can be very difficult as it requires accurate identification and the expertise of a pest control contractor.

(Above) **Black garden ants swarming inside a building**

Bees and wasps

Wasps frequently nest in attics and other voids and can cause serious nuisance. If a nest is treated to kill the wasps, but not removed, it can lead to other pest problems: carpet beetles and spider beetles will live and breed on the dead adult wasps and larvae in the old nest. Although bee nests are rarer in houses, bees do occasionally nest in disused chimney flues. The first sign may be honey running into the fireplace followed by bees buzzing around the room. It can be a very difficult job to remove these nests, but if they are left, the dead bees and larvae will provide food for carpet beetles and spider

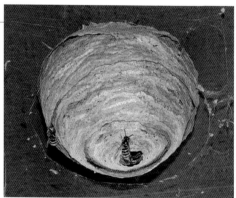

(Above) **An active wasp's nest in an attic**

beetles. There have also been instances of large wax moth larvae (called *Galleria*) migrating into rooms from a bees' nest in the flue.

It can be difficult to proof chimneys and attics to prevent wasps and bees from nesting without compromising ventilation. Blocked flues may also cause damp problems as the airflow is restricted. Removal of old nests is really the only way of avoiding future pest problems.

Mason bees are very different from honey bees as they burrow into soft stone to make an individual nest cell. They normally tunnel in soft limestone and hard sand, but can sometimes be found in large numbers living in the mortar between house bricks. As they are not able to bore into sound mortar, an infestation of mason bees in a chimney is usually a sign that it urgently needs repointing. The bees may be doing you a favour by telling you that your chimney is about to collapse.

(Above) A honey bees' nest removed from a chimney flue

Ground beetles

There are many types of ground beetles (called Carabidae) and many are predators forming an important part of the food chain. They range in size from very small beetles less than 3mm long to some of Britain's biggest beetles over 25mm long. Many are black, but some have an attractive metallic sheen. Although their natural home is outdoors, they are often found coming into houses under doors. It is possible that they do this to shelter from the rain and then cannot find a way back out. They will do no harm to

twice actual size

the structure or contents of a building, although the larger ones are very active and can cause alarm. They are also often found on sticky pest traps that have been placed near doors and it is possible they are attracted to the other insects caught on the trap.

Harlequin ladybird
Harmonia axyridis

actual size

Ladybirds have been using our homes to hibernate during winter months for hundreds of years and are generally welcome as useful predators of greenfly and other garden pests. In 2003, however, a new species of ladybird was recorded in the UK and has since become a serious nuisance. Originally from the Far East, the harlequin ladybird, *Harmonia axyridis*, probably spread to Britain on nursery plants from Europe. Once here, it rapidly became established in south-east England and has steadily spread northwards in the last 15 years.

It is similar to our native seven-spot ladybird, but is much larger. The common form is red with 19 black spots and cream on the head and thorax, but there is also a black form with 2 or 4 red spots. They will hibernate in houses, sometimes in very large numbers, and being larger than native ladybirds, they are much more obvious. The adults produce a nasty yellow liquid when disturbed which will stain paint and furnishings. Although they are efficient predators of garden pests, harlequin ladybirds compete with native species and may even eat them when food is short. For this reason they are regarded as an unwelcome alien species which should be controlled where possible. Removal of the hibernating adults with a brush and vacuum cleaner is the best option.

(Below left) **Harlequin ladybirds can gather in large numbers to hibernate inside houses**
(Below right) **Two examples of the black variety of the harlequin ladybird**

Woodlice

These are not insects, but belong to a group called the Crustacea which also includes shrimps and crabs. They have many legs and a series of overlapping plates covering the top of the body.

actual size

A number of species, such as *Porcellio* (pictured here), which are greyish-brown and range in size from a few millimetres to 15mm, will come into buildings. They live outdoors under stones, in damp vegetation and in rotting wood and cannot survive for long in dry conditions. They are often found in basements or near doors and windows where they have wandered in from damper outdoor environments. Most soon die of desiccation without causing any damage, although dead woodlice could provide a food source for other pests. A persistent problem of live woodlice indoors, however, should be investigated as it may indicate that there is high local humidity and rotting wood.

Spiders

Spiders are not insects but are arachnids and have eight legs. Although they are not considered pests, they can cause alarm to some people. There are several different species commonly found in houses in Britain, including the common house spider *Tegenaria*. Both web spiders and hunting spiders will catch insects, including pest beetles and moths, and are generally beneficial.

(Above) **A false widow spider – an efficient predator of small insects**

In Britain there are only a few species, such as the false widow spiders (*Steatoda* sp.), which will occasionally bite humans. Despite wide media attention and alarmist reporting, they do not pose a significant risk. Although it is true that they can inflict a painful bite, they are not aggressive and when disturbed will usually run away. Common house spiders can get quite large and they are often seen in the autumn when the males roam around houses looking for a mate. They can be alarming, but are harmless to humans.

Prevention and control of invertebrate invaders

Many different types of invertebrates can invade our homes. Most can be kept out by identifying entry points and proofing to stop them getting in. Some seasonal invaders can be very persistent, however, and are difficult to keep out. Treatments may be necessary in such cases. Dead insects should always be removed to prevent secondary infestations.

(Right) **Ground beetles, Devil's coach-horse beetles, centipedes and millipedes caught on a trap inside a house where they came in through a gap under a door**

Key points for preventing ant infestation:

✓ **Maintain hygiene standards.** Make sure food (especially sugary or sweet food) is not left out, and is stored in airtight containers. Make sure any crumbs or spills are cleaned up promptly.

✓ **Prevent entry.** Insecticide dust can be used as a barrier on air bricks or other entry points. Barrier chalk may also be effective in preventing access by worker ants.

✓ **Use poison bait to eradicate persistent nests.** Killing worker ants with an aerosol insecticide is not effective as there will be thousands more workers in the nest to replace the ones killed. Persistent problems in places such as conservatories may be dealt with by using poison ant bait which is taken back to the nest by the workers and should eventually eradicate the whole nest. Very little can be done to deter flying ants.

Key points for preventing other invertebrate invaders:

✓ **Stop invertebrates from gaining entry.** Fly screens can be very effective. Make sure there are tight seals around doors and windows.

Rodents have been taking advantage of man's hospitality since the dawn of civilisation. They are probably the most successful and abundant mammals on earth, although the vast majority of species hardly ever come into contact with man. Some, however, collectively known as the 'commensal' rodents, have taken advantage of the way we live and rely upon sharing our food and housing. Not only will they damage our possessions, but they can also spread disease, sometimes to devastating effect.

The most important rodent pest in houses in Britain is the house mouse, *Mus domesticus*. The brown or Norway rat, *Rattus norvegicus*, arrived in this country in the 18th century and is common in some urban and rural areas, but rarely causes problems inside houses. Ship, roof or black rat (*Rattus rattus*) was more common in the past, but is now only found in a few city locations in Britain. Other occasional invaders are field mice, wood mice, squirrels and edible dormice.

(Below) **A pair of common house mice taking advantage of spilled grain**

House mouse
Mus domesticus

The house mouse is thought to have arrived in Britain on boats from the Continent, probably in the Iron Age, about 2,500 years ago. House mice are variable in colour from grey to almost black with a slightly lighter underbelly. Their tails are about the same length as their body and head. Adult house mice rarely weigh more than 20g and have a combined body and head length of 70–90mm. Because they are shy and usually nocturnal, the animals themselves are rarely seen. Finding droppings and other signs of mouse activity is the usual indication that mice are present. An adult mouse will produce about 50 droppings per day. The droppings are spindle shaped and about 3–7mm long. As mice do not defecate in specific places, the droppings can be distributed over a wide area. Mice will also urinate everywhere and although this may not be visible, the urine can transmit diseases, such as food poisoning, by contaminating work surfaces and utensils. Male mice will also use urine to mark territory. Large numbers of mice will produce a very characteristic musty, unpleasant smell.

Once mice have become established in a building, the population can expand rapidly if there is shelter,

Mousetraps

One of the earliest descriptions of mousetraps in Britain was by Leonard Mascall, Clerk of the Kitchen to the Archbishop of Canterbury in the 16th century. In his book of *sundrie Engines and Trappes to take Polcats, Buzards, Rattes, Mice, and all other Kindes of Vermine*, written in about 1590, he describes how to make live capture traps, deadfalls and snap traps, all forerunners of the types we use today, as well as several different recipes for rodent poisons. Modern snap traps, first patented in 1894, are still one of the most effective and humane ways of eliminating small numbers of mice.

(Right) **Baited snap traps are simple, but effective. Mice usually prefer chocolate or raisins to cheese**

water and sufficient food. In ideal conditions one pair of mice can produce a litter of six offspring up to eight times in one year. Given that mice can be sexually mature in just over 40 days, this means that one pair of mice

has the potential to give rise to several hundred offspring in a year, causing a population explosion: 'a plague of mice on your house' is a curse which can very literally be fulfilled.

When breeding, the female mouse will shred any available material to make a nest. Mice have front incisor teeth that grow all the time and they must gnaw on hard materials to keep them sharp and prevent them from overgrowing. The incisors have a thin outer layer of hard enamel and a softer layer of dentine on the inner surfaces. The hard outer enamel wears away more slowly than the inner surfaces, producing a sharp chisel-like end to

the incisors, perfect for gnawing through even the hardest materials. This gnawing behaviour can result in damage to food packaging, books, textiles and furniture and despite their small size, the destruction they cause can be extreme. Electrical wiring and alarm systems are also susceptible to attack, and a number of electrical fires in houses have been caused by rodents gnawing the electrical systems and causing a short circuit.

(Above) **Mouse droppings are small – the 20p coin gives an idea of their size**
(Below) **Electrical wiring damaged by mice**

Prevention and control of mice

The successful control of a large and serious mouse infestation will undoubtedly require the services of a specialised pest control contractor. The householder, however, can do a lot to prevent mice getting into a building and discourage them from living and breeding there.

(Above) **A female house mouse and her babies in a nest incorporating shredded paper, as well as natural materials**

Although prevention is always better than control, if you do get mice in the house you will need to get rid of them as soon as possible to prevent their becoming established. The most effective way to deal with a small number of mice is to use 'break-back' traps. Success will depend upon setting the right number of traps in the area where the rodents are moving and placing the traps correctly. They should be placed against a wall or solid barrier along which the rodents run. This will help to ensure that mice will activate the traps as they walk into them. Including food will help to attract mice to the trap, and contrary to popular opinion, cheese is not the most attractive bait. Alternatives such as peanut butter, dried fruit and chocolate are more effective. Make sure pets and children cannot get at the traps. Traps should be checked every day and dead mice should be put in a bag and disposed of as soon as they are caught. Always wear rubber gloves when removing nests and handling any dead rodents or contaminated objects as they can carry diseases.

Many people prefer to use live traps rather than the more effective break-back types. The trapped mice should, however, be disposed of humanely: it is not recommended that they are released back into the wild as this is not their normal habitat. A mouse released into the garden will quickly find its way back into the house.

Sticky boards can be effective as a last resort when used correctly by a qualified contractor, but they are considered inhumane by many and their use by amateurs is not recommended.

The use of rodenticides for controlling mice requires great care. You should always read and adhere to any instructions on the label and every precaution should be taken to ensure that the poisons are not accessible to children, pets or non-target wild animals. One of the problems with using poisoned rodent baits is that the mice will often die in inaccessible places. This can not only lead to unpleasant smells, but the mummified remains also provide a substantial source of food for clothes moths and carpet beetles.

(Below) **This historic book has been severely damaged by a female mouse shredding the paper to make her nest**

Although cats may keep mice at bay, some domestic pets are too well fed and lazy to bother with chasing mice. Sonic deterrents are rarely effective as the mice soon get used to them and ignore them.

If you decide that a rodent problem is too difficult or daunting, seek advice from a pest control contractor. They should be a member of the British Pest Control Association (BPCA) where membership is dependent upon regular standards audits and employment of trained and qualified technicians.

Key points for the prevention and control of mice:

✓ **Proof buildings against entry.** Mice will be more inclined to try and get into houses when the weather gets cooler in the autumn and winter. They can squeeze through very small gaps, and if you can push your little finger under a door or in a gap between windows, then an adult mouse can get in. They will also climb through holes in air bricks and through gaps left around pipes and cables. Some of these gaps can be proofed with fine metal mesh or wire wool to prevent mice getting through. Doors can be fitted with bristle strips, but these must be checked regularly as mice can gnaw an entry hole in them.

✓ **Store human or animal food in hard plastic or metal sealed containers.** Food left uncovered overnight is an open invitation for mice to feed, but even food in boxes and packets can be easily attacked. Mice will quickly gnaw through anything that is not hard plastic or metal to get at the food inside. Keeping food in mouse-proof containers is the first step to stopping them living with you. Do not forget pet and bird food which is equally, and sometimes more, attractive to mice. Bulk purchases of dried food stored in cellars, garages or outhouses are also very vulnerable to attack.

✓ **Regularly check undisturbed places for mouse nests.** Once inside, mice will seek somewhere warm and undisturbed and only venture out into the open when they are searching for food. They have been known to nest in floor voids, in and under kitchen cupboards and even behind fridges and freezers where it is warm. If you hear the patter of feet at night, then check the attic as mice will often nest there in cardboard boxes, packaging or rolled up carpets. Also check cellars, outbuildings and garages, inside boxes and other materials that have been stored for a while. Mice have even been found nesting in an old unused computer. A regular trip to the recycle centre to dispose of unwanted materials will help avoid giving mice a good home.

✓ **Avoid putting out crumbs or other human foods for birds.** Large amounts of freely available food will encourage mice, as well as rats.

✓ **Look out for droppings.**

✓ **Look out for gnaw marks and damage caused by chewing.**

Brown rat
Rattus norvegicus

Rats can reproduce at only five weeks old and, in ideal conditions, can have up to five litters per year, all year around, so populations can expand very quickly. They require sources of food and water to thrive, so restricting access to water tanks as well as to stored food, food waste, and scraps, seeds and grains intended for birds, is the best way to discourage an infestation.

If you suspect that there are rats in the area then it is worthwhile checking the drains and sewers for breaks and faults. Contact a specialist for advice if you find large droppings and signs of rat runs.

(Right) **Rat droppings are larger than mouse droppings – the 20p coin gives an idea of size**

Grey squirrel
Sciurus carolinensis

Grey squirrels, native to North America, were released into parks in Britain in 1876 and by the early 1900s had become established throughout the country.

Many people like to feed squirrels, but they can cause significant damage and nuisance if encouraged, particularly if they gain access to your house. They can get in through the eaves or cracks in tiles and can live in roof spaces where they build their nests (dreys). Squirrels can damage the outside of buildings when trying to gain access and their gnawing can also damage electrical wiring and water piping in roof spaces.

Squirrels can be a particular problem for thatched buildings, where they can dig into the thatch (see page 97) causing considerable damage.

Any action against squirrels should be undertaken by a pest control contractor and carried out humanely.

Edible dormouse
Glis glis

A native of southern Europe, edible dormice were considered a delicacy by the Romans, and it is from this that their name derives. They are attractive animals and were deliberately released into the wild in Britain in Tring, Hertfordshire, by the naturalist Walter Rothschild in 1902. They are now well established in the Chiltern Hills area around Tring, but do not appear to have spread further.

They are grey with dark rings round the eyes and a bushy squirrel-like tail and are much bigger than Britain's very small native dormouse (known as the hazel or common dormouse, *Muscardinus avellanarius*). They hibernate in the winter and can cause problems when they take up residence in attics as they can be noisy and may also gnaw wiring. So if you live in the Chiltern area and hear noises in the attic in the autumn and winter, you may have a family of edible dormice as lodgers.

Control and proofing to stop them getting in is best left to an expert.

Bats

Bats may be found roosting in attics and roof areas of older houses and outbuildings. There are many species, but the pipistrelle is the most common in Britain. Although their alkaline urine can cause damage to surfaces, dried bat droppings are not such a hazard as other animal droppings, as they mainly comprise undigested chitin from insect bodies. Although bat droppings, particularly those of smaller bats, appear similar to those of house mice, they are easily distinguished from rodent droppings as they crumble into shiny, dusty insect fragments when crushed. Accumulations of butterfly, lacewing and other insects' wings on an attic floor is a sign of an active bat colony.

(Above) **Lesser horseshoe bats roosting and flying in a roof space**
(Below) **Bat droppings and insect wings below a bat roost in an attic**

All species of bat and their breeding sites or resting places (roosts) are protected under the Wildlife and Countryside Act 1981. It is an offence for anyone intentionally to kill, injure or handle a bat, to possess a bat (whether live or dead) or disturb a roosting bat. It is also an offence to damage, destroy or obstruct access to any place used by bats for shelter, whether they are present or not.

Small bats can get caught on sticky insect monitoring traps. This could result in prosecution. If traps must be used in areas where bats are active, they should be covered with a wire mesh cage to prevent bats touching the sticky surfaces.

Exclusion by proofing should only be undertaken following specialist advice from someone who understands bats and their ecology. If bats are suspected in any areas where timbers are to be treated with insecticides, or where renovation or development work is to take place, the relevant statutory conservation body should be contacted. In the United Kingdom no action may be taken against bats without prior approval from Natural England or the Bat Conservation Trust.

BIRDS

Birds are an important part of our environment and many of us enjoy watching them and encouraging them into our gardens. Birds nesting or roosting on, or even in, houses can, however, cause a great nuisance with their noise and droppings, and with insects living in their nests. Even old nests can house insect pests which may then invade other parts of the house. Feeding birds can be well-intentioned, but may also encourage rats and mice, particularly if human food scraps are put out.

A number of bird species have adapted well to living in the urban environment, and can develop very high population levels which have a significant effect on the buildings and people living in and around them. Feral pigeons, *Columba livia*, are the most numerous and troublesome.

Feral pigeon
Columba livia

Feral pigeons can breed throughout the year. Nests are built in or on buildings, under eaves or any other structures that provide support and protection. They are usually found on ledges or in hollows and, in time, and with repeated use, these can become filled with pigeon droppings and debris. Up to four broods may be reared during a year with one or two chicks per brood.

Feral pigeons normally feed in flocks and become highly efficient at taking food when it is left unattended for short periods. They rely mainly on spillage around food preparation areas or on food (including bread, cake and seeds) given, spilt or discarded

(Right) **Feral pigeon roosting on a ledge behind poorly placed proofing spikes, with a build-up of droppings and feathers**

by people. The size of a feral pigeon population in an area is directly related to the amount of food available.

Feral pigeons can transmit a range of diseases, including ornithosis (a form of psittacosis) and there are proven cases of humans catching the disease from pigeons. Feral pigeons can also carry the food poisoning bacteria Salmonellosis and, although its incidence is low, this public health hazard should not be ignored.

Most damage caused by feral pigeons arises from their infestation of buildings where populations can build up to high levels. Fouling and contamination of structures and statues can occur where the birds nest, rest or roost. This is not only unsightly, but their acidic droppings cause erosion of stonework and mortar. Old droppings can also produce foul smells and may cause allergic reactions in some people. Accumulations of droppings can become infested with large numbers of bird mites and insects. The mobility of feral pigeons means that they are able to transmit these infestations from one building to another. Debris and dead birds can also be a food source for flies, moths, beetles, and other insects, as well as blocking flues and rainwater pipes with subsequent extensive damage.

Other birds

In addition to pigeons, many different species, including collared doves, rooks and jackdaws, may nest, or attempt to nest, on chimneys. Nest material and birds falling down chimney flues are a frequent source of insect pest problems in houses. Capping of chimneys and installation of deterrent spikes will usually solve the problem if they are well maintained.

Nesting house sparrows have occasionally caused problems in the past, but the large decline in the sparrow population has now reduced the risk. Martins, swifts and swallows will frequently nest in the eaves of buildings. Their nests will harbour some insects, but these rarely cause problems to the occupants of a house, although bird parasites, such as martin bugs (*Oeciacus hirundinis*), may come into houses and have occasionally bitten humans when the fledglings have left their nest.

Prevention and control of pigeons and other birds

With the control of most rodent and insect pests, emphasis is usually on reducing or eliminating the population. With birds, successful damage prevention is more likely to be achieved through environmental manipulation and prevention of access than by attempts to directly reduce the population. This is because birds can easily and rapidly move into areas from which other birds have been removed. The high population of pest species in urban areas provides a reservoir of birds that can rapidly replace those removed. The most effective method of managing a pest bird problem is the removal of the food source attracting the birds, together with selective application of proofing measures.

(Below) A considerable accumulation of bird nest material in a roof space

In many countries strict laws exist to protect birds and restrict the ways in which they can be controlled. In the United Kingdom all birds are protected. Legislation does, however, allow for certain species to be culled under particular circumstances, especially when there are risks to health and of transmission of disease.

Removal of large quantities of nest material, droppings and dead birds can be hazardous and should only be undertaken by a qualified cleaning contractor.

Key points for feral pigeon prevention:

✓ **Restrict availability of food.** One of the main reasons that feral pigeons are attracted to an area is availability of food. Reduction in food supply remains the single most effective method of reducing feral pigeon populations locally. In houses that are open to the public, notices explaining why feeding pigeons is unacceptable can be effective, particularly if it is pointed out that the pigeon food can also attract rats and mice, all of which can carry diseases.

✓ **Proof buildings or structures against access or entry.** Birds may enter houses, either inadvertently or intentionally, seeking shelter and warmth. They will foul the interior and may set off alarm systems. To prevent birds getting in, all openings in excess of about 20mm should be closed. Roofs should be kept in good repair and holes or missing tiles replaced. The eaves of many buildings can be sealed with rolled up wire mesh which still allows airflow. Where possible, permanently open windows, ventilators and any other openings should be proofed with wire mesh or netting.

Feral pigeon problems in the 'wells' of buildings can be solved by blocking bird entry with netting or by stretching wires across the top of the well at about 30cm spacing, to prevent the pigeons flying into them. This second technique is particularly useful when netting might exclude light.

Netting is a very effective technique for excluding birds from almost all areas

(Above) **Discreet bird netting and spikes protect the sculptures of the Marble Arch, London**

(Above) **Sprung bird wires prevent birds from roosting on ledges**

where their access may cause problems. It can be very cost-effective, although requires maintenance. The use of nets simply involves stretching bird-proof netting across any opening that needs to be blocked. It is essential that the correct size mesh is used and 50mm mesh is appropriate for feral pigeons. Netting can also be used to protect statues, ornamental stonework and alcoves and, if installed well, can be very unobtrusive.

✓ **Use repellents and deterrents.** A product known as 'fire gel' has recently been developed. Although the precise mechanism is not clear, this harmless gel, placed in small plastic dishes attached onto buildings, appears to act as a visual deterrent, discouraging pigeons from landing or roosting on adjacent ledges. Results with this gel have been mixed, although it appears to have been successful on some buildings.

The use of blunted spikes can be particularly effective in preventing birds roosting and nesting on chimneys. If it is aesthetically acceptable, spikes can also be used on windowsills and ledges as long as the spike density is sufficient and the spikes are well secured to the sills.

All proofing systems require regular inspection and maintenance to ensure ongoing effectiveness and safety.

✓ **Predatory birds.** The use of predatory birds, such as Harris hawks, to scare feral pigeons and other pest species has become popular in recent years and can be very effective. Those flying the birds need to be very skilled and, if it is to be successful, requires regular and repeated exposure of the predator to the birds causing the problem.

Culling. The mobility of pigeons, their high population densities and their high reproductive rates in urban areas, means that population reduction techniques are rarely effective. The control of any bird population by culling is strictly controlled by legislation and should only be carried out by qualified professionals.

(Above) **Birds of prey, such as this Harris hawk, may be used to deter problem birds**

NEW INSECT INVADERS

Many of the insect pest species that are now ubiquitous in our homes were originally introduced to the British Isles from overseas. The Romans, for example, may have introduced case-bearing clothes moths (see page 26) and some food pests, and in later centuries German cockroaches, grain beetles, webbing clothes moths (see page 24), harlequin ladybirds (see page 71) and many other species arrived with goods on ships from around the world. Some have become so well established in dwellings they now are regarded as indigenous species. More recently, a new wave of invaders is being documented, their spread across Britain perhaps facilitated by milder winters and warmer summers.

(Above) **Harlequin ladybirds emerging from hibernation**

Australian carpet beetle
Anthrenocerus australis

New species of textile pests which have become established in Britain, and which have been mentioned previously, include the Guernsey carpet beetle (see page 35) and the vodka beetle (see page 36). A closely related species, which has only recently been found attacking textiles in the United Kingdom, is the Australian carpet beetle *Anthrenocerus australis*. This small, dark, round beetle resembles

🐛 actual size

the other carpet beetles *Anthrenus*, but has thin bands of white hairs instead of scales.

(Right) The larvae of Australian carpet beetle

The larvae are dark and hairy and very active. This carpet beetle species was probably introduced in wool imported from Australia in the 1930s and occasional specimens were found in houses and warehouses over the next 60 years. In 2010, however, an infestation was discovered in an office carpet in the Victoria and Albert Museum, London, and adults and larvae have since been found in two historic houses in London.

This beetle is a serious pest of textiles in Australia and it is therefore important that any new infestations are recognised and recorded. Because *Anthrenocerus australis* is superficially so similar in size and appearance to the other *Anthrenus* carpet beetle species, however, it may well be under-reported in Britain.

Grey silverfish
Ctenolepisma longicaudata

actual size

A species of silverfish called *Ctenolepisma longicaudata* has recently been identified as a threat to houses and collections in the United Kingdom. Known as the grey silverfish, this insect is now a common and serious pest in Austria, the Netherlands and other parts of Europe.

The first infestation in England was recorded in a house in Reading, Berkshire, in 2014. Since then it has been found in museums, galleries and archives in London, Birmingham, Gloucester and Portsmouth.

It is much larger than the indigenous silverfish *Lepisma saccharina* (see page 53) and has very long antennae and tail bristles. The grey silverfish appears to be able to survive at lower humidity than *Lepisma* and causes serious damage to paper. This silverfish, therefore, potentially poses a much greater threat to collections kept in houses.

House longhorn beetle
Hylotrupes bajulus

A number of species of wood-boring beetles are regularly introduced into Britain in wood imported from other countries. The auger beetle *Sinoxylon* has been known to completely destroy picture frames imported from India, and other wood-boring beetles have emerged from items of furniture imported from Asia. Because these beetles need high temperatures to breed, however, they cannot establish a foothold here.

actual size

One serious wood-boring beetle pest which has gained a foothold in England is the house longhorn beetle *Hylotrupes bajulus*. In the 1930s it was recorded attacking roof timbers in a number of houses in Surrey and it was regularly found in this area over the next 30 years.

It is a large beetle with long antennae and leaves characteristic oval holes when it emerges from the timber. The larvae can cause enormous damage to timber, mainly attacking sapwood. Because of the serious risk to property it is one of the few insects subject to building regulations. In the last few years a number of house longhorn beetles have been recorded emerging from furniture and fittings imported from Europe and it is important that any sightings of this potentially devastating species are reported.

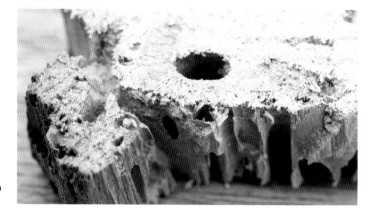

(Right) Section of a roof beam severely damaged by house longhorn beetle

Future threats?

Warmer winters and hotter summers may also allow other pests, which cannot at the moment succeed in the British Isles, to be become established here. The most serious potential threat is from subterranean termite *Reticulitermes* which is now well established in Europe as far north as Paris. A single infestation was found in north Devon in 1996 and a determined effort was made to eradicate the population. In 2010, however, a small surviving termite colony was found in the same area and has been re-treated.

Termites can cause devastating damage to building timbers and it is vital that they do not become established in Britain.

(Above) **Timber frame destroyed by termites**

PEST MANAGEMENT GUIDE

The horrifying discovery that a favourite item of clothing or piece of furniture has been infested and damaged by insects or other pests is often the first time that people become aware that they have pests in the house. Pest damage does not occur overnight, however, and is usually an indication that pests have been there for a while, making themselves at home, completely unnoticed.

Integrated pest management (IPM) is a process of identifying pests at an early stage and preventing them from living in your house and multiplying. Grabbing a can of insecticide is not usually the right answer: understanding the most appropriate methods for prevention and treatment is the best way of keeping your home and treasured possessions safe from pests.

Successful control of hygiene pests such as cockroaches, bedbugs and fleas usually requires specific techniques and treatment methods carried out by specialist contractors (see page 120).

Recognising the problem

Where do pests live?

Many of our pests are indigenous to the British Isles and can survive outdoors in the winter in sheltered locations. Others, such as webbing clothes moth, will not overwinter outside and need to live in houses all year. In warmer weather, many insects can fly around and come into houses through open windows and doors.

Most pests like to live in dark, undisturbed places, particularly where there is organic dirt and debris. This means that attics, cellars, little-used rooms and cupboards are ideal homes for pests to thrive and increase unnoticed.

(Left) **A wool rug from Brodsworth Hall, damaged by clothes moths. The damage is concentrated in the lighter area which lay under a piece of heavy furniture. The furniture protected the rug from dirt and fading, but provided a habitat where the larvae could feed undisturbed**

Unused chimney flues are less obvious places, but have proven to be one of the most common sources of pests in historic houses. Infestations of clothes moths, carpet beetles and spider beetles develop in old bird nests and within the carcases of dead birds which have become lodged in flues. Once established in the flue, insects can drop down the chimney and then crawl or fly out into the rooms below, leading to a wider infestation. A large infestation of biscuit beetles in a dining room was traced to old bread crusts which had been dropped down the chimney by birds.

Even rooms that are used and occupied can harbour pests if they are provided with a suitable place to live. Fitted wool carpets are the most common source of infestation by clothes moths and carpet beetles. Open areas that are walked on and regularly cleaned are never infested; the insects live in parts of the carpet that are hidden and undisturbed. Favourite spots are under heavy furniture that is rarely, or never, moved, at the edges where carpet may be turned under, and under stair rods on stair carpets. Wool underlay at the edges of carpets is an ideal habitat for moths and beetles as it is dark and never disturbed. Carpet in fitted wardrobes and bathrooms can also be a perfect place for pests to live.

(Above) **A cluttered attic is an ideal home for wood and textile pests, and a potential nesting place for birds and mice** *(Below)* **It is difficult to clean fitted wool carpet where it sits under heavy furniture, such as this bed at Eltham Palace, creating an ideal habitat for clothes moth and carpet beetle larvae**

Upholstered furniture can also provide a home for pests, even when it is used. Moth and carpet beetle larvae can live undetected in horsehair and wool stuffing and their presence is only detected when the adult moths or beetles emerge to fly around in spring and summer. They will also live in cushions stuffed with feathers and may bite their way through cotton covers to get out. Upholstered furniture which is not used regularly is more at risk and insects may live in creases and crevices or under decorative binding or fringes.

(Above) **Wool felt upholstery damaged by carpet beetle larvae**

Wool, fur and feathers are all good food for pests, and items of clothing which have been stored for long periods are particularly at risk. Boxes of old clothes on top of wardrobes or in attics may well have moths or beetles

Insects are not just for Christmas

The fashion for Christmas decorations made from natural organic materials has been known to lead to some interesting seasonal infestations.

In one case, biscuits and gingerbread men were stored in a box for two years and then brought out in December to hang on a Christmas tree. They were full of holes made by emerging biscuit beetles and there was a layer of dead beetles and frass in the paper wrapping.

In another case, moths flying around an attic room in a historic house were traced to a large number of stored Christmas decorations made from dried oranges which had become infested.

These types of decorations should be stored in airtight containers and checked every year. If they become infested, they should be treated by freezing or disposed of.

living in them and eating large holes. Pieces of wool carpet stored in cupboards or in the attic are also prime sources of food for textile pests. Wool insulation can cause problems as it provides an undisturbed source of food for clothes moths and other pests.

Areas of persistent dampness, such as damp basements or cellars, cupboards against north-facing walls or behind blocked air bricks, or unheated outbuildings, can harbour damp-loving pests such as silverfish, booklice and fungus and plaster beetles. Damp timbers, either in the structure of a building or in furniture and other objects, provide a perfect habitat for furniture beetle, deathwatch beetle and even wood weevils.

Stored food or other organic material can harbour biscuit beetles or Indian meal moths and inadequately stored food and food waste can attract flies, mice, rats or pigeons who may take up residence nearby to take advantage of a readily available source of food.

With the right environmental conditions, pests can exploit any opportunity they find within your house for an easy meal.

(Below) **Wood objects and furniture stored in damp outbuildings can easily become infested by wood-boring insects. Cluttered storage makes cleaning and checking objects impossible**

Thatch

Thatched roofs made from reeds or straw can provide a cosy home for many pest species including rodents, birds and insects.

A well-maintained thatched roof will not result in many pest problems, but if it is neglected, animals will take advantage and take up residence. Mice, rats, squirrels and birds are obvious invaders; less obvious inhabitants will be woodlice, springtails, silverfish, flies, wasps and other insects. Jackdaws and crows have been known to attack thatch because they are searching for hibernating cluster flies living inside it. Birds will also remove straws for nesting material. Some birds will also use a thatched roof as a handy nest site and squirrels have been known to use them to bury nuts.

Netting is the main way to deter larger pests, such as birds and rodents, from gaining access and causing damage. Rats living in thatch require a source of water to drink and will often take advantage of open water tanks in loft spaces, so make sure that these are always covered.

Keeping a thatched roof in good condition and regularly inspecting it for early signs of pest activity is the best way of preventing pests from becoming established.

(Below left) **Neglected thatch can provide a good home for pests**
(Below right) **Well-maintained thatch with a wire net cover will result in few pest problems**

Signs of pest activity

Pest management should not be simply a reaction to the discovery of insect damage. As well as looking out for actual insects themselves, alive or dead, being vigilant for signs of pest activity is the first priority in avoiding pest problems. Visual checking is important, so look in places where insects might live for signs that they are in residence. Infestations of flies, ants or ladybirds are usually fairly obvious, but their secretive habits make other invaders harder to spot.

Wood-borers: Gritty frass under wood beams or furniture can be a sign of wood-borers, but it is important to determine if it is old or fresh. Good housekeeping in March to remove old dirt and debris will make fresh frass more obvious when adult beetles emerge.

If there are already emergence holes in timber or furniture it can be very difficult to decide if these are old or new. Pasting tissue paper over affected areas in early spring will mean that beetles have to bore through the paper and will then leave a readily visible emergence hole. New holes can be marked and the level of infestation can be recorded (see page 50). This technique has been used in some historic houses to show that population levels of furniture beetles and deathwatch beetles gradually dropped after carrying out remedial work to prevent damp ingress.

Carpet beetle and clothes moth larvae: Infestation of carpet beetles in items of clothing can result in small, neat holes, whereas moths leave larger, irregular holes and grazed fabric with silky webbing. Carpet beetle and clothes moth larvae will produce gritty frass

(Below) **Frass at the base of old books indicates that they are being eaten by insects**

when they feed which may drop down below hanging garments. A pale-coloured or white surface will make this more visible as the colour of the frass will be the same colour as the object being eaten.

Carpet beetle larvae regularly shed their skins as they grow and finding casts stuck to clothing, carpets and upholstery is a sign that the larvae have been feeding. Webbing clothes moth larvae produce strands or tubes of silk stuck to the material being eaten and case-bearing clothes moth larvae leave empty silk bags or cases behind.

(Above) **A carpet damaged by clothes moths**
(Below) **Silverfish damage to the paper lining pasted inside a damp wooden box**

Food pests: Infestations of food pests, such as biscuit beetles and Indian meal moth, will result in the presence of silk webbing, frass and small bore holes in packets and food items.

Damp-loving pests: The presence of damp-loving pests, such as silverfish and booklice, is often indicated by evidence of grazed or abraded paper and wallpaper.

Rodents: Droppings, gnaw marks and scampering sounds in the attic may be the first signs of rodents.

Case study: Furniture beetles in a historic house

In early June, staff at a small historic house with a very good housekeeping and monitoring programme discovered 15 adult furniture beetles on windowsills in a room where they had not been found before.

When the windowsills were checked two weeks later there were 16 new beetles. All the wooden objects in the room were carefully checked and, although there were signs of old damage, there were no recent emergence holes or fresh frass. In addition, we knew that the relative humidity in the room rarely went above 60%. No more beetles were found in July, showing that that year's emergence was probably over. In late July the room and its contents were checked again, revealing no evidence of insect activity until we looked up the chimney. The flue had been blocked by a hardboard panel with a wooden frame, riddled with fresh woodworm holes.

The infested board was removed and replaced with a metal mesh screen and the problem was solved.

(Above) **Adult furniture beetle**
(Below) **Fresh emergence holes in the wooden frame blocking the chimney flue**

Key lessons:

✓ *Regular monitoring and recording of pests is key to catching a new infestation early before the problem can become established. Sometimes it is the discovery of the adult insects themselves, rather than the damage they have caused, that is the first sign of a new pest problem.*

✓ *Check the room thoroughly to discover the source of a fresh furniture beetle infestation, looking in even the most unlikely places. Removing the infested object is often the simplest way of getting rid of a new infestation.*

Detecting pests

In any scheme of pest management, correct identification of the pest species is key to successfully preventing or treating an infestation.

The most effective method for detecting insects is by using sticky traps, which can either be used to bring to light an existing pest infestation, or to monitor for new problems.

Sticky traps

Most pest insects are very small and secretive making them difficult to find, and this is why sticky insect traps can be very useful for discovering if you have pests. They can be used to monitor insects such as carpet beetles, spider beetles, silverfish, booklice and other crawling insects. Placing a few sticky 'blunder' traps around the house will give you some indication of the number of crawling pests which are in the building.

Traps should be placed on the floor in the angle against a wall, preferably in corners where they will catch more wandering insects. Cardboard traps are more effective, but plastic floor traps are more durable and, because they are low in height, can be tucked under shelves and furniture.

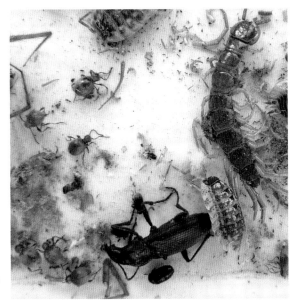

(Below) **Examples of actual pests – spider beetles (on the left of the image) – caught on a sticky trap alongside a variety of non-pest species**
(Bottom) **Sticky trap placed against a wall to monitor for pest insects**

Check traps at least every three months using a magnifier to examine what you have caught, as most pest adults and larvae are small and some species can look very similar. The glue should remain effective for six months to a year, depending upon the trap type. Traps placed near outside doors will capture insects coming into the house from outside. These may need to be replaced more frequently if they become covered with woodlice and ground beetles.

(Above) **Webbing clothes moths caught on a sticky pheromone trap**

Pheromone lures

If you start to catch moths on your traps, or if you have seen them flying around, you can use a trap with a non-toxic attractant lure, which makes the traps far more effective. These lures use the sex attractant pheromone produced by the female moths to attract males. Each type of moth produces a unique pheromone and so it is important to identify which moth species is present, and to use the correct pheromone lure. Most of the pheromone traps available are for the webbing clothes moth *Tineola bisselliella* and they can be extremely effective. The males are stimulated by the pheromone and fly towards the traps, where they get stuck.

Traps can be suspended or placed on shelves and will give early warning of infestation or an indication of the severity of the infestation.

When temperatures are high enough to promote flight, up to 20 times as many moths may be caught on traps with pheromone lures as on unbaited ones. When temperatures are below 18°C the males are reluctant to fly and suspended traps may be less effective. In these situations, pheromone traps can be put on the floor where they will catch more male moths than unbaited ones.

Specific pheromone lures for case-bearing clothes moth *Tinea pellionella* (see page 26) and Indian meal moth *Plodia interpunctella* (see page 28) are also available.

As traps with pheromone lures will catch many more moths than unbaited traps, do not panic if you find a lot more moths initially when using pheromone traps for the first time.

(Above) **Two traps from the same room. The one on the right has a pheromone lure, which has attracted and caught a larger number of clothes moths than the unbaited trap on the left**

Warning

✘ Sticky cardboard traps should **NEVER BE USED** in rooms where bats may be present as they can become entangled and get stuck on the glue.

Solving the problem

The secret to successful long-term pest management is to prevent infestations before they become established, but many preventative techniques will also have the result of solving an established problem. An understanding of the conditions different pests need in order to thrive will help you to combat them, by making your home an inhospitable habitat, removing sources of food and places for them to live and breed.

Controlling temperature

Insect pests cannot regulate their own body temperatures and their rates of growth and reproduction are determined by the temperature of their surrounding environment: the warmer it is, the faster insects feed, breed and multiply. Temperatures of 20°C and above will suit most pests and many houses are kept warmer than this. In unheated houses, insects will become less active and then dormant in the autumn and winter. When temperatures rise in the spring they become active and adults will start to emerge and move around. In most cases they are not newly arrived as many people think, but have been waiting, unnoticed, in the house until conditions are right for them to emerge.

Heated houses are frequently warmer in the winter than they are in the summer and this provides ideal conditions for species such as webbing clothes moths to breed all year round. At 25°C there may be three generations of moths per year and with each female laying up to 100 eggs, populations can rise very quickly. Lowering the temperature a few degrees in rooms with vulnerable items will reduce the risk of damage.

(Below) **Turning down the heating by just a few degrees will make a house less attractive to some pests**

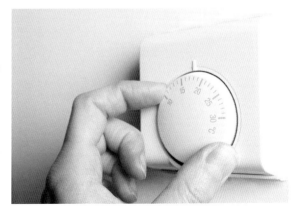

Controlling humidity

A number of the most significant insect pests need damp conditions to thrive. Furniture beetle, *Anobium punctatum*, for example, needs high levels of moisture in the wood and relative humidity above 60% (see page 52) to successfully breed and multiply. In modern housing, furniture beetle has therefore become quite rare due to the increased use of central heating which has reduced average humidity levels. It is usually only found infesting wood in unheated houses, damp basements and attics or in outbuildings and in objects which have been recently stored in damper conditions. Bringing infested wood into drier conditions will not stop adults emerging, but they will not be able to spread and attack drier wood already in the house.

Deathwatch beetles have a complicated life cycle and are rarely found in modern houses. They will only cause serious problems in oak and other hardwood which has become damp enough to sustain fungal growth.

Wood weevils require even higher levels of moisture in the wood and are only a problem where timber is very damp. Silverfish will only breed rapidly and cause serious problems in damp conditions of above 70% relative humidity. They are often found, therefore, in damp basements or in localised damp areas.

If there are a lot of pests indicating serious damp issues, then it is advisable to call on expert advice. An experienced surveyor will measure relative humidity levels and moisture levels in wood and identify the sources of the problem. High levels of moisture can be caused by many factors, such as condensation, poor damp proofing or leaks from roofs, gutters or water pipes and these should all be checked and remedied.

(Below) **A badly maintained downpipe has allowed water to saturate the wall behind it, which could lead to pest problems within the building**

Removing dampness will go a long way to preventing and treating infestation by a wide range of pest species. It is also important to ensure there is adequate ventilation, particularly in under-floor voids, so it is vital to ensure that air bricks are not obstructed. Dehumidifiers can be used to temporarily reduce moisture levels in rooms, but are rarely a long-term solution.

(Above) **Blocked air bricks will prevent proper air circulation and lead to increased dampness**

Regular housekeeping

Because insects are small they can find food in relatively small areas which may not be immediately obvious. This means that cleaning and good housekeeping are the most important contributors to successful pest prevention. Pests thrive in a dirty environment where organic debris and rubbish provide shelter as well as food.

Humans shed kilograms of skin, hair and clothing fibres every year and this provides food for pests unless it is regularly removed. Historic houses with a heavy footfall from visitors are particularly vulnerable. Household pets can also shed large quantities of cat fur and dog hair which will feed the pests. Cooking and dining supply additional sources of human food, as crumbs and spills get into

corners and crevices, or fall through cracks in floorboards, ending up in voids and dead spaces and providing food for pests. Regular vacuum-cleaning, particularly the use of crevice tools, is the main weapon in the fight against household insect pests.

Old rodent and bird nests can support moths, spider beetles and carpet beetles. There have been many cases where old bird nest material and debris left in blocked-up chimneys, heating ducts and other dead spaces, has provided a source of food and harbourage for insect pests, which have then infested carpets, furniture and curtains. It is essential to keep chimney flues clean and have them properly capped to stop birds roosting or nesting.

Old wasp and bee nests can also cause problems and should be removed where possible.

(Above) **Blocked chimney flues prevent good air circulation, leading to dampness, and allow bird nest material to build up, both of which can encourage pests**
(Below) **Removing a bird's nest from a ventilator**

Case study: The battle of the beetles at Brodsworth Hall

Brodsworth Hall in Yorkshire is a special place with an unusual history. The present Hall was built in the 1860s by Charles Sabine Augustus Thellusson and is a magnificent example of what can be bought with a large inheritance from banking, slavery and colonial trade. The family's fortunes dwindled, however, and by the time the Hall came into the guardianship of English Heritage in 1990, it had been badly neglected for over 30 years.

The lack of maintenance had led to decay and destruction of Brodsworth's stone, timber and building fabric and considerable damage to the house's unique contents. A five-year battle against the agents of decay, including rot and insects, then ensued before English Heritage reopened Brodsworth Hall to the public in 1995. Roof timbers damaged by wood-boring beetles were replaced, and room fittings with active furniture beetle infestations were treated with insecticide sprays and fumigated with methyl bromide (an effective treatment, but one that can no longer be used). The moveable house contents were taken off-site for treatment and most of the wool textiles, which were infested with clothes moths and carpet beetles, were treated by freezing. Objects were carefully conserved and returned to the house uninfested.

Continual seepage of water into the house had led to extensive silverfish damage to the wallpaper in some of the ground-floor rooms. Remedial work has stopped the water ingress and the walls are no longer damp, but the damaged wallpaper has been left in situ to show the ravages of neglect.

Ongoing monitoring

The insect monitoring programme started at Brodsworth in 1998 and traps showed that, in spite of all the remedial work, there were still pockets of infestation surviving in the house. Carpet beetle adults and larvae were found in some rooms and large numbers of golden spider beetles were found on traps near fireplaces. This indicated that there were still quantities of organic debris in the chimney flues. Although the chimneys had been cleaned, they contain inaccessible ledges where bird nests and dead birds can accumulate. The debris is almost impossible to remove now that small boys cannot be sent up chimneys to clean them out. The chimneys have been re-swept many times over subsequent years, and there has been a

(Right) **Repair work to Brodsworth Hall in the 1990s included replacing the decayed and damaged roof**

gradual decline in the golden spider beetle population as their food source has diminished.

The remedial work to eliminate water ingress resulted in a dramatic decline in silverfish numbers. They are, however, still present in the house in some parts of the ground floor and service wing where there are higher levels of moisture. Stable, low numbers of silverfish can be tolerated, but their numbers are monitored: an increase of these pests would indicate that the environmental conditions in the house had changed and would need to be investigated.

The devastation that can be wrought on wool textiles and taxidermy by clothes moths and carpet beetles has been combatted by a regular and comprehensive regime of excellent housekeeping by the house staff. Regular thorough cleaning of the rooms to remove hair, fluff and other organic debris keeps the carpet beetle and case-bearing clothes moth populations to low levels. It is essential to maintain these high standards to prevent the few remaining moths and beetles from increasing in numbers again and causing further damage. There are still pests in Brodsworth Hall, but with good housekeeping they do not pose a great risk to the fragile collections.

Key lessons:

✘ *Years of neglect of a historic house can lead to devastating damage to its structure and contents by pests, which can only be remedied by considerable conservation work.*

✔ *Regular monitoring and checking, coupled with excellent housekeeping regimes, are needed to prevent pests from increasing in numbers and causing further irreparable damage to collections.*

(Right, all) These three photographs from Brodsworth Hall show some of the problems caused by neglect of the building. Water seeping into the house caused significant damp and the resulting mould and insect infestations damaged the structure of the building, its fittings and contents

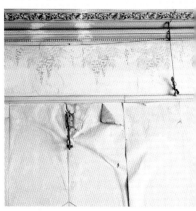

Areas to check and clean include:
- Unused chimneys and blocked fireplaces
- Bird, wasp and bee nests in attics
- Heating and ventilation ducts
- Cavity walls and floors
- Heater boxes
- Unused rooms or cupboards, particularly in attics and basements
- Gaps between walls and floors
- Dead spaces behind and under storage furniture, bookcases and plinths
- Dead spaces under and behind storage shelving
- Felt lining in boxes and felt sealing strips on doors
- Under furniture on carpet

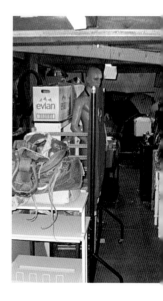

Bird, rat and insect droppings can provide food for pests and should be removed to prevent the development of damaging insect pests, bacteria and moulds. Mould can also encourage fungus-feeding insects, such as silverfish, plaster beetles and booklice.

Cluster flies, ladybirds and lacewings will hibernate over winter in houses and their dead bodies provide a good food supply for the larvae of carpet beetles and spider beetles. If cluster flies and other insects cannot be kept out by proofing, they should be removed by vacuuming at frequent intervals.

Even in houses with very good programmes of pest management, a moth infestation can become established in the void under floorboards. Hair and other organic debris falls through the floorboard cracks and accumulates in the void below, providing a substantial source of food for moth larvae in a warm, dark environment. In some cases mouse bodies have provided an additional source of protein. Unfortunately, the only lasting solution is to lift the floorboards and clean the void underneath which can prove very time consuming and expensive.

(Top) **Crowded store rooms, such as this, can contain many objects that are at risk of infestation, and should be checked regularly for signs of pest activity** *(Above)* **Frequent vacuuming with a crevice tool removes dirt and insects from the edges of fitted carpets: a favourite location of insect pests**

Insect music lovers

Musical instruments may not seem obvious as food for pests until you examine what they are made from.

Pianos are particularly vulnerable as they contain large amounts of wool felt which can be eaten by clothes moths and carpet beetles. The glue used to attach the felt is usually animal-based, which adds to the attraction. Many other instruments, including pipe organs, woodwind and brass, contain felt pads that can be eaten by moth and beetle larvae. The quills in harpsichords, and the animal protein gut strings and hair bows of stringed instruments are also at risk.

Old instrument cases are even more likely to be infested than the actual instruments themselves, as they are often lined with felt attached with animal glue. A closed, dark case in a warm cupboard or attic provides a perfect environment for clothes moths and carpet beetles. Damp wooden cases may also be eaten by furniture beetles. Insect pests can occasionally be found living in fluff balls of hair and other organic debris that accumulate inside stringed instruments, particularly double basses.

Exotic musical instruments brought from overseas, often hung on a wall or stored away and forgotten, can also be attacked. Some years ago, a fashion for animal skin drums led to an outbreak of 'African drum moth'. These were identified as *Tinea translucens*, a larger African relative of our case-bearing clothes moth *Tinea pellionella*.

Wooden instruments kept in cool, dry conditions will not be at risk from attack by furniture beetles, but can be badly damaged if left untouched for years in a damp attic or basement.

Fortunately, there is a simple remedy for preventing pests damaging musical instruments: regular cleaning, keeping them in cool, dry conditions and above all, playing them regularly. Moths and beetles will not live in a piano which produces loud vibrations, so banging out a few discords every week will keep the pests at bay.

(Top) **Moth damage to an animal skin drum**
(Right) **Carpet beetle damage to the felt lining of a violin case and to the strings of the bows**

Repellents

A number of natural products, such as camphor and citrus oils, have been used to deter indoor pests since Ancient Greek and Roman times. The rise of the chemical industry in the 19th century led to the availability of cheaper and more effective repellents, such as naphthalene and paradichlorobenzene. These were used for many years, often in the form of the classic 'moth balls'. Although they were effective at high doses in deterring adult clothes moths, they had less effect against larvae developing deep inside textiles. In addition to their objectionable smell, there have been concerns about the safety of breathing in the toxic fumes emanating from wardrobes and drawers where these chemical repellents were being used, and most have now been banned as repellent insecticides.

(Above) **Lavender, rosemary and cedarwood, which contain natural repellents, can be used to deter adult insects**

Because of this there has been a resurgence of interest in repellents based on natural materials. Many of these are now on sale, including those using lavender, rosemary and cedarwood – some of the same plants recommended by medieval herbalists. There is evidence to show that these will repel adult moths at high concentrations, but that the effect can wear off quickly as the volatile repellent chemicals evaporate. They will also have little effect on larvae feeding inside folded textiles. Fresh lavender has also been used in some houses in the autumn to deter cluster flies from entering because, unlike bees, the flies do not like the smell of lavender.

Insect traps

Although traps are mainly used for detection and monitoring of insect pests (see page 101), some types can be used to control particular pests. Ultraviolet fly killer traps can be effective in some situations, particularly against houseflies and cluster flies (see page 66). Sticky traps can be used to catch flying insects that stray into the house, but will rarely catch enough insects to reduce a population of established pests.

Proofing and physical barriers

Proofing your house to stop pests getting in is the best way to prevent an infestation of rats, mice, grey squirrels and pigeons. The main measures include the use of netting and wire, blocking gaps around pipes and cables and ensuring doors and windows seal closely. Slipped tiles and loose flashing can provide an easy entry for rodents and birds into a roof space. Unused chimneys should be capped to prevent birds and their nest material from falling down and providing food for other pests. Birds of prey, if deployed regularly, can deter many pest birds. Fly screens can be used to keep out airborne insect pests.

Quarantine

It is always advisable to check new items coming into a house from a place where they might have become infested with insects, such as a sale room or outbuilding. There is clear evidence, for example, of Guernsey carpet beetles being introduced into a house in the north of England when a large number of items of furniture and taxidermy were moved there from a house in London. Thorough checking and treatment of infested items in a freezer or humidity controlled heat chamber before the move would have prevented this.

(Above) **Chimneys fitted with bird spikes to prevent roosting and nesting**

Treatments

Sometimes, simply altering environmental conditions and carrying out preventive measures are not enough to get rid of an established pest problem. In these cases a remedial treatment will be necessary. Some of the methods set out below can be carried out at home. For more serious infestations, particularly of rodents, birds or human parasites, it may be necessary to call in the experts (see page 120).

Freezing

Carpet beetles and moths seem to particularly target expensive cashmere, wool jersey and felt in jumpers, cardigans, suits and other items. Washing affected clothes at low temperatures of 30°C may not kill all insects and so freezing is the recommended method for dealing with an infestation of insect pests. The best and most effective solution is to wrap the items in plastic bags and place them in a freezer at -20°C for at least two weeks. After this time all eggs, larvae, pupae and adults will be dead and the items can be gently brushed and vacuum-cleaned and then stored in sealed bags. This is very important to protect them from reinfestation from adult moths or beetles which may be flying around and laying eggs.

Any freezing programme must be carefully planned to ensure everything is treated and does not get reinfested. If there are large numbers of infested items to be treated, this can be carried out in a commercial freezer for two weeks at -20°C, or three to five days at -30°C (see page 116–17 for a step-by-step guide to the freezing process).

Infestation of carpets and upholstery is more difficult to deal with because items may be too bulky to fit in a domestic freezer. A walk-in commercial freezer or large flat-pack freezer can be used for these objects.

(Below) **Wrapping infested objects in plastic sheeting ready to put into the freezer**

Always ensure that items to be treated are wrapped and sealed in plastic and not unwrapped until after they have returned to room temperature to avoid condensation damage.

Heating

Heat can be used to kill insects, and temperatures of between 52° and 60°C will kill all pests in 24 hours. Many companies offer a bagging and heating service, but this is generally designed to kill infestations of bedbugs and the heating cycle has little or no control of humidity. This may be acceptable for mattresses or robust items of upholstered furniture, but is not suitable for vulnerable historic objects.

Heat treatment of these objects requires close control of humidity during the heating cycle to avoid damage by shrinkage or condensation. This can be achieved over 24 hours for a wide selection of materials in a commercial ICM® (Integrated Contamination Management) fixed or mobile chamber.

Insecticides

There are a wide variety of different insecticidal chemicals available for different pests in different situations. It is important to choose the right one and vital to always read labels and follow manufacturer's instructions before use.

A plague of flies or other flying insects can be difficult to live with and the only quick solution is to use an aerosol insecticide. Make sure you use one that rapidly knocks down and kills adult insects. There are many products on the market based on natural pyrethrins or synthetic pyrethroids which are effective insect nerve poisons, but have a low toxicity to humans. Although these are effective for killing adult flying insects, they do not persist for long enough to kill larvae or adults that are hidden away.

Total release aerosols

Total release aerosols (or 'bombs') can be used in attics or other large voids to deal with cluster flies, but must not be used if bats are present. Although these sorts of aerosols

Freezing to control insect pests in small items

This is a general guide for freezing small items in domestic freezers. For larger items or accessioned museum collections, refer to the English Heritage freezer guidelines at www.english-heritage.org.uk.

Low temperature treatment is the safest and most effective way of killing textile pests, such as clothes moths and carpet beetles. It can also be used to treat books and most paper and wood objects. It is very important, however, to follow these guidelines to avoid damage from condensation.

To kill all adults, larvae, pupae and eggs, freezer temperatures must be maintained at -18°C to -20°C for 14 days.

Preparation

- Infested items should not be cleaned before freezing. Items must be cleaned after treatment. This will help to avoid further spread of any insect eggs or larvae.
- It is essential to wrap items before freezing to ensure that condensation does not form on them when they are removed from the freezer. Plastic self-sealing bags, large plastic bags or plastic sheeting can be used.
- Place the object in the plastic self-sealing bag or wrap it in the plastic sheeting. Try to remove excess air if possible.
- Seal plastic sheeting with tape to ensure that no air or moisture can enter.

(Above) **Labelling a wrapped object before freezing. The label should include the date of freezing**

(Above) **Placing a wrapped object carefully into a chest freezer**

- Fragile or awkwardly shaped objects can be placed in a tray or a box, which can then be wrapped in plastic sheeting.

Freezing

- Place items carefully into the freezer. Do not pack them in too tightly and try to ensure there is an air space around the sides.
- Baskets can be used in chest freezers.
- Leave items in the freezer at between -18°C and -20°C continuously for 14 days.
- Items need only be left in a -30°C freezer for three to four days.

(Above) **Large-scale freezing treatment of infested objects at Brodsworth Hall**

PLEASE NOTE: *Always use freezer gloves and avoid contact with frozen surfaces to prevent freezer burn when handling objects at -30°C.*

After treatment

- Remove items carefully: many materials can become very brittle at low temperatures.
- Once they have been removed, place the items on racking or a non-absorbent surface and allow them to return to room temperature for at least 24 hours before unwrapping. Very dense objects should be left for at least 48 hours.
- Do not worry if you see condensation on the outside of the bag when items are first removed. As long as the moisture does not come in contact with the objects, it will not cause damage.
- After items have returned to room temperature, they can be unwrapped and cleaned by gentle brushing and vacuuming to remove dead insects or larvae and any other signs of infestation, such as frass and webbing.
- After treatment, items should be stored in sealed bags or boxes to prevent reinfestation.

Large infested items, such as upholstery, rugs and carpets, can be treated in a commercial walk-in freezer. The same guidelines for wrapping and exposure times apply, but larger items will take longer to reach the target temperature and to come back to room temperature after treatment.

When to call in the experts

Many of the pest prevention techniques described in this book can be carried out by amateurs. There are occasions, however, when it is necessary to get advice from, or call in, the professionals. For information and advice on finding a fully qualified and professional pest control service, contact the British Pest Control Association for details of all BPCA accredited members: **www.bpca.org.uk**

Other specialist organisations may be helpful for specific pest issues, as set out below.

Bats. Bats are protected and you must not attempt to come into contact with them or try to remove them. For specialist help and advice contact the Bat Conservation Trust, your local bat society, or Natural England: **www.bats.org.uk**
www.gov.uk/government/organisations/natural-england

Bedbugs and cockroaches. These pests pose a risk to human health and control should always be carried out by a specialist pest control company.

Bees. If honey bees are nesting in your building, contact a local bee expert or the British Beekeepers Association for advice and help: **www.bbka.org.uk**. If mason bees are attacking your mortar, get it looked at by a professional builder.

Birds. A serious infestation will require the services of a specialised pest control contractor as birds are protected. Extensive proofing measures including installation of nets, wires, spikes and capping should also be installed by a contractor. It is also advisable to use a professional cleaner to remove large quantities of birds' nests and droppings.

Chimney cleaning. Cleaning chimney flues is a tricky job in historic houses and there are specialist companies who will carry this out. Contact the Guild of Master Chimney Sweeps to find an accredited professional: **www.guildofmasterchimneysweeps.co.uk**

Deathwatch beetles. Where there is a serious active infestation, particularly in roof beams, you should employ a professional specialist surveyor to assess the problem and take moisture measurements. Remedial structural work may be needed as chemical treatments are rarely effective if moisture problems are not rectified.

Fleas. Make sure the fleas are identified correctly and seek advice from your local veterinary surgery for serious cat or dog flea problems. The Natural History Museum offers an insect identification service: **www.nhm.ac.uk**

Flies. For serious and persistent problems, call in a specialist contractor to get the flies identified accurately before any remedial treatment is carried out. Extensive proofing may also require the services of a specialist.

Heat treatment. Historic collections should not be treated in a simple heat bag. Use a professional company who carry out controlled humidity treatment, for example the ICM ® system: **www.icm.works/en**

Large-scale freezing. Large-scale freezing treatment against moths or carpet beetles will need to be carried out by a specialist and with advice from a conservator if collections are historically important or fragile. Many of the larger museums offer a large-scale freezing and quarantine service.

Mice. A serious and persistent mouse problem will require the services of a professional pest control company. They may also advise on proofing and other prevention measures.

Other mammals and wildlife. Getting rid of squirrels from inside a building will require the services of a specialised pest control contractor. Most species of British mammals are protected and so, if in doubt, contact the BPCA for advice and help.

Rats. It is rarely possible to successfully control rats without the help of a professional pest control company.

Valuable and vulnerable items, such as musical instruments and veneered and inlaid furniture. If you suspect that these are infested and need to be treated, get advice from an accredited conservator sourced through the Institute of Conservation (Icon) Conservation Register: **www.conservationregister.com**

Wasps. Disposal of an active wasp nest and removal of old nests will often require the services of a specialised pest control contractor. Serious health incidents have occurred when people have tried to remove nests themselves.

Woodworm/furniture beetle. If you have established that there is an extensive active infestation of furniture beetles, the affected areas should be surveyed to determine the extent of damp problems. Remedial work may be needed before considering chemical treatments as these are rarely effective if damp issues are not rectified first.

If you do carry out your own treatments, it is essential that you always read the labels of any chemical products before use.

Further reading

P Ashe and JP O'Connor *Irish Indoor Insects: A Popular Guide* (Town House, Dublin, 2000)

O Booy, H Roy and M Wade *Field Guide to the Invasive Plants and Animals of Britain* (Bloomsbury, London, 2015)

R Edwards and AE Mill *Termites in Buildings: Their Biology and Control* (Rentokil Library, Rentokil Ltd, East Grinstead, 1986)

R Jones *House Guests: House Pests* (Bloomsbury, London, 2016)

P Marren and R Mabey *Bugs Britannica* (Chattow and Windus, London, 2010)

I McCaig and B Ridout (eds) *Timber: English Heritage Practical Building Conservation* (English Heritage and Ashgate, Farnham, 2012)

H Mourier and O Winding *Collins Guide to Wild Life in House and Home* (Collins, London and Glasgow, 1986)

G Ordish *The Living House* (Revised edition) (Vintage, London, 1985)

DB Pinniger *Integrated Pest Management in Cultural Heritage* (Archetype Publications, London, 2015)

WH Robinson *Urban Entomology* (Chapman and Hall, London, 1996)

Websites

British Pest Control Association: **www.bpca.org.uk**
English Heritage Trust: **www.english-heritage.org.uk**
Historic England: **www.historicengland.org.uk**
Historyonics: **www.historyonics.com**
The Institute of Conservation: **www.icon.org.uk**
The Integrated Pest Management Working Group: **www.museumpests.net**
Natural History Museum: **www.nhm.ac.uk**
What's eating your collection? (Collections Trust and Birmingham Museums): **www.whatseatingyourcollection.com**

ACKNOWLEDGEMENTS

A special thanks to Darren Mann and Katherine Child for providing many of the superb insect photos. Thanks to Nigel Blades, Bob Child, Amy Crossman, Adrian Meyer, Pascal Querner, Jane Thompson Webb and Carol Wilson for sharing information and images. Thanks also to Edward Pinniger for checking the text so carefully. Last, but not least, we would like to thank the English Heritage staff who have worked so diligently with us since 1997 to make IPM work so well in their properties.

PICTURE CREDITS

All images © Historic England unless otherwise stated. Cutaway drawing (inside front cover) by John Ronayne. Diagrams by Hannah Faux (adapted from original drawings by David Pinniger): 19, 23, 41, 53. Maps by Martin Brown (data supplied by www.whatseatingyourcollection.com). Pest logos by Martin Brown. Other images by permission of: **Basement Stock/Alamy Stock Photo:** 10 top. **John Black/www.bats. org.uk:** 82 top. **Bob Child:** 54 bottom. **John Critchley (Source: Historic England Archive):** 108, 109 top, 117. **Anders Leth Damgaard/www.amber-inclusions.dk:** 16. **DBP Entomology:** 14, 15, 21, 22, 26 bottom, 27 top, 27 bottom, 32 bottom, 33 bottom, 34 bottom, 39, 40, 42 top and middle, 44 bottom left, 45, 47 bottom, 48, 49, 52 both, 53 middle, 57 bottom, 62 bottom, 63, 65 bottom, 67, 68 top, 69 both, 71 bottom both, 73, 76 bottom, 78, 82 bottom, 86 right, 89 top, 90 bottom, 95 top, 97 left, 98, 99 bottom, 101 both, 103, 105, 107 both, 110 both, 111 both, 116 left, 118, 119. **DBP Entomology (courtesy of Kelmscott Manor):** 50, 54 top, 100 bottom, 113. **DBP Entomology/Mike Brown CSL (contains public sector information licensed under the Open Government Licence v3.0):** 20 top, 20 bottom, 23 top, 28 bottom, 55 bottom, 56 top left. **English Heritage Trust/OUMNH:** 24 top and bottom left, 26 top and middle, 27 middle, 28 top and middle, 33 middle, 35 all, 36 all, 41 top, 42 bottom right, 44 top, 46, 53 top, 55 top, 56 right top, middle and bottom, 57 top, 59 both, 60 top and middle, 61 top, 65 top, 68 bottom, 70 bottom, 72 top, 88 bottom, 90 top, 100 top. **Everett Collection Inc/Alamy Stock Photo:** 11. **Getty Images:** 6 (DEA/V. Pirozzi/De Agostini), 7 (photo by SSPL), 12 (Stephanie Aglietti/AFP), 37 (John Downer). **Les Gibbon/Alamy Stock Photo:** 51. **Graces Guide to British Industrial History:** 10 bottom. **Loes Knoop:** 89 bottom. **Dee Lauder:** 3 bottom. **Manor Photography/Alamy Stock Photo:** 18. **Adrian Meyer:** 76 top, 80 middle. **Minnesota Historical Society:** 62 top. **Natural History Museum, London/Science Photo Library:** 8 bottom. **Nature Photographers Ltd/Alamy Stock Photo:** 77. **TJ Nelson:** 38, 71 top, 72 bottom, 87. **David Pinniger:** 3. **Shutterstock:** 31 (bondarchuk), 60 bottom (Marek Velechovsky), 64 (Barnaby Chambers), 74 (Chloe Langton), 75 top (IrinaK), 75 bottom (moritorus), 80 top (scooperdigital), 80 bottom (Jeremy Alan Baxter), 81 (marcovarro), 83 (Nil Kulp), 88 top (IanRedding), 91 (EmEvn), 95 bottom (Kalloo), 104 (Daisy Daisy), 112 (Irina Fischer). **Smithsonian Libraries (Biodiversity Heritage Library):** 9 top. **The Trustees of the British Museum:** 17. **Wellcome Collection:** 8 top (CC BY 4.0 licence).

Every effort has been made to trace copyright holders and we apologise for any unintentional omission, which we would be pleased to correct in any subsequent edition of the book.